GORSE, BROOM
AND
HEATHLANDS

CHRIS HOWKINS

Published by
Chris Howkins

1

PUBLISHED
Chris Howkins
70 Grange Road
New Haw,
Addlestone
Surrey
KT15 3RH
www.chrishowkins.com

PRINTED
Hobbs the Printers Ltd.
Brunel Road
Southampton
Hampshire
SO40 3WX

COVER PHOTOS
European Gorse
Front: *Chris Howkins*
Back: *Mary Adler MBE*

2

CONTENTS

INTRODUCTION

People have given our heathlands an amazing history stretching back over 4,000 years. Instead of viewing them as scrubby set-aside areas, as we tend to see them today, they worked them throughout the year as a vital renewable resource. How they managed that on such poor soils was the question that led to a review of the uses of the heathland plants, published in 1997, as *Heathland Harvest.* That book is now out of print but the sections dealing with heather, both *Calluna* and *Erica,* with other relevant material, was extracted, updated, enlarged and published as *Heathers and Heathlands* in 2004. The same revision has now been given to the Gorse and the Broom.

This volume concentrates upon 'Lowland Heath' in Southern England but on occasions looks further afield. The material has been pieced together from hundreds of documentary references, wherein there has sometimes been only the briefest of mentions and so not all these have been footnoted. Conjectural material is stated as such. Minor uses of the plants have been kept minimal so as not to exaggerate their importance. Thus broom has been sourced as a green dye, and its tannins for tanning leather, while the fibres have been used for paper and cloth making (for which the Spanish Broom, *Spartium junceum,* has been used more widely) while the hard wood was exploited in the distant past for darts and spears and more recently for veneers since the wood is beautifully veined.

It could be argued that many of the uses of gorse and broom are poor quality expedients for marginalised people with a poor standard of living. Alternatively, it can be argued that the range of uses shows an admirable understanding of cropping the poor soils as a renewable resource to sustain families and communities for thousands of years. The yearly cycles of management for gorse and broom ran concurrently with cycles for heather, birch, bracken and whortleberry, while heaths with wet areas had seasonal extras from sundew, bog asphodel, bog bean, bog myrtle and *Sphagnum* mosses. It was all highly intricate and intensive, making heathland a landscape of value to any manor.

4

FURZE AND GORSE

The Species

Gorse, whin or furze are the three commonest names for one of the most distinctive heathland shrubs; the only one that is covered with very sharp spines so that anyone who doesn't know a daisy from a dock will know when they have found this! To a botanist furze is not one species but three, but our ancestors invariably referred to them as one. All are spiny with yellow flowers.

By far the commonest, and most robust, is the Common or European Gorse, *Ulex europaeus* L, which is the prime species of the old records. It likes the maritime climate of the British Isles and on the Continent does best within the influence of the sea, in Portugal and Spain, France and Belgium, and south western Scandinavia. Towards Central Europe it is an introduced species that has naturalised, despite being cut back hard by severe frosts. It has been introduced to other countries around the world, such as New Zealand which it loves and has become a problem weed. On British heathlands the gorse, and associated wildlife, is therefore rather special and is of importance when the European lowland heaths are reviewed as a whole.

The second most important species to our ancestors was the Western Gorse, *Ulex gallii* Planchon. It is often said to be smaller, maturing at just 10cm but it can, and usually does, grow much taller, up to 200cm, the same as Common Gorse. It lives up to its name and prefers the western, more maritime half of the country although it does grow around the East Anglian coasts within the ameliorating effects of the sea. It is not common on the Continent either, being restricted largely to S. W. France and Spain. Whereas Common Gorse can start flowering around Christmas in a mild winter and is usually over by June, the Western Gorse flowers from July to September.

The third species is Dwarf Gorse, *Ulex minor* Roth, which usually gets you round the ankles but can reach 100cm. It is densely spined and very sharply so. It often associates with the Bell Heather, *Erica cinerea* L., and flowers at the same time in late summer, making a magnificent ground cover of purple and yellow on dry heathland but only in the south and the eastern half at that.[1]

5

Gorse
Ulex europaeus

6

Inset Portraits Artist:
Janet Blight

7

Broom, *Cytisus scoparius* (L) Link., waves great armfuls of golden blooms around its head like a joyous pilgrim in some grand medieval procession. It even smells a bit medieval to some people while others love the tang it puts in the air. It attracts bees which feed on its pollen but there is no nectar. Formerly it was a commonplace shrub. In the 17th century when Evelyn thought of "barren" places they were for *'Fern, Broom and Heath etc.'* [2]but he does not think of Furze – areas of Furze were cropped and valued rather than being barren. Broom grew also in the pools of sunlight in open woodland, coppice woods and around wood pastures. Thus the medieval *Ballad of Green Broom* which begins, *"There was an old man lived out in the wood ,/ And his trade was the cutting of Broom, green Broom ..."* which of course does not say that the Broom was in the wood but later, *"Jonny arose and slipp'd on his clothes / and away to the wood to cut Broom."* The demise of such managed woodland sites has restricted the broom considerably.

The Names

Gorse, furze and whin are all ancient names brought by early colonisers. It was possibly the Scandinavians (Vikings and Danes) who brought the word 'whin' for it has persisted particularly well in regions which they colonised, such as parts of Ireland. In some places whin is used regularly in the plural as whins. The Germanic peoples (Angles, Saxons, etc.) brought the names 'gorse' and 'furze'. Oldest is possibly gorse, which is thought to derive from the Indoeuropean word 'ghrzd' which meant rough or prickly. Furze was also descriptive, coming from old words for plants with evergreen needles, hence 'firs' for conifers. These are the names of long standing which have changed little through the centuries, being short, easy to remember and easy to use. There are a few newer British names such as Fingers-and-Thumbs or Thumbs-and-Fingers, French Furze, Honey-bottle, Pins-and-needles. It's even been called Ling like the *Calluna* heather. Country people know it widely and simply as *fuzz* or *goss*. In many counties it was invariably furze or fuzz in the records until c.1900 and then usage changes suddenly to gorse, which has persisted ever since.

Broom
Cytisus scoparius

9

Broom comes from the Old English *brom* and thus arrived with Germanic peoples from the Continent. The shrub was so highly valued that many places took their names from it – see the index of a British road atlas for a list of places beginning with broom or brom. In the areas not colonised by the Germanic peoples the old British name persisted, as *banadle* in Wales, whether as banhallen in the South or banadlen in the North, while the Cornish *banathel* survives as bannel or banathal in place-names.

The Whinchat takes its name
from the whin or gorse bushes it loves.

10

FOLKLORE OF GORSE AND BROOM

To get the greatest appreciation of the meaning of these plants to our ancestors we need to understand their spiritual values as well as their everyday practical values. The two aspects were inseparable in the past and each influenced the other. Gorse and broom have both had a long association with man and so it is not surprisingly that each is rich in ancient folklore. Much of it is now shared between them but may well have been distinct once. Confusion could have arisen as traditions declined and with more people losing their affinity with the land as they became increasingly urbanised.

The folklore dates back to pre-Christian times and suggests an association with pagan fertility rites. Thus the month of May figures importantly and that was the time of many fertility rituals. The Christians endeavoured to stamp this out and so only fragmentary material survives, whether for individual species or for the seasonal rituals in general. It would make sense if this association were so because the prime fertility ritual centred upon the winter solstice and the rebirth of the sun to bring another year's harvest. Gorse was used in at least some of the regional rituals at this time of the year, such as the children's performance from parts of Wales and Ireland, on 26th December, known variously as Hunting the Wren, King of the Wren or King of the Birds, when a piece of gorse bush was carried at the head of the procession.[3] From Devon Lafonte[4] records that sprigs of gorse were placed in a pot and decorated like a little Christmas tree, as a substitute for that prime fertility plant, the mistletoe. The link with fertility persisted in the name of this Christmas feature – the 'kissing bush'.

Hardly are the midwinter rituals over before the gorse can be unfurling its first blooms, as though to prove that the rituals have been successful, that fertility has been carried from the dying old year through the solstice to be reborn in the New Year. Although the Christians were very successful at expunging references out of written material, they had no control over folk songs and many of these contain material many centuries old. A particularly popular theme centres upon an unmarried girl collecting gorse or broom flowers and scattering them around her lover's head (and sometimes feet) as he slept. She ensured that upon waking she was the first

11

person he saw and the flowers ensured he would fall in love with her, marry her and of course live happily ever after. The more flowers the more children they would have[5] Thus in the ballad *Broomfield Hill:*

Take ye the blossom of the broom,
The blossom it smells sweet,
And strew it at your true-love's head
And likewise at his feet.[6]

Even where folk song has died out there are references to these concepts in idiomatic English as in these three examples:

When Gorse is in bloom
Courting is in season.

When Gorse is out of bloom
Kissing is out of season.

Furze is only out of bloom
When kissing's out of tune.

We get a clue to this being devolved from ritualised concepts from the fact that, despite the popularly held view, gorse can not usually be found in bloom throughout the year. It has led to later variants such as, *I'll pay my debts when gorse is out of bloom* (Gloucestershire) and *While furze is in bloom England shall never be conquered* (Devon). Several writers have recorded the Devon belief that it is unlucky for a girl to marry before an elder sister, unless the younger bride steps over a bunch or faggot of gorse placed across the threshold of the couple's new home. This is known as 'dancing the furze faggot'. There are versions of this involving a broom rather than a faggot. When a woman left a broom against the doorpost it was a sign that her husband was away and that gentleman callers were welcome. If the man leant it there it was a sign that the wife was away and that his mates were welcome to come round for a few beers. To avoid unfortunate confusions it depended which doorpost was involved! The people I have asked about it nowadays can no longer remember with certainty which is which but it would be in keeping with other traditions if the woman used the left doorpost and the man used the right doorpost.

Reinforcing the probability that these plants were of spiritual importance is the taboo on bringing them indoors as cut-flowers. This is particularly so for broom but obviously the pliant stems lend themselves to such usage far more than the rigid spiny gorse. My Welsh mother was devout in her following of this tradition, saying I was *not* to pick broom on any account because it was the home of the fairy queen and she'd not like it. The one day I *did* pick broom and bring it indoors my father had an accident at work and of course I got the blame (and punishment) for that. This is an old idea found in the medieval ballads, e.g. in *Tam Lin:*

> *Out then spake the Queen o' Fairies,*
> *Out of a bush of broom.*[7]

References to a being in a broom bush survive in written form from at least the 13th century. Relegating the old spirit forces to mere fairies became universal in later Christian times. In Hampshire it was dragons that were believed to live in gorse thickets and so it was dangerous to even touch the bushes.[8] The taboo was to be respected fervently during the month of May – the second time in the year of fertility ritual importance, to welcome in the summer and the prospect of another harvest. It is also the main month for the flowering of the broom, as a counterpart to the late winter flowering of the gorse. However, the taboo was upon bringing gorse or broom indoors at all, whether in flower or not. Thus Lafonte records that in Devon gorse could not be used as a household fuel during May. It would be interesting to know whether this was ever practiced. Universally it has been held as bad luck to bring them indoors, even in isolated communities such as on the Channel Islands.[9] To do so would bring death or poverty or hunger along with them. However, it was safe to decorate the *outside* of homes with these flowers and indeed in May it was wise to do so. They were included among the hawthorn and other blooms as 'the may' – the flowers that were hung up over the doors etc. to ward off evil forces, whether fairies or witches or dragons or whatever.[10] Witches are still represented as flying away on a broom.

13

Beyond the house, farmers said that heavy flowering of the broom foretold heavy cropping at harvest time, while another tradition says that when the broom finishes flowering love has left the land, as though this was a sign to end the fertility rituals for that season. The Christian Church abolished those in favour of the ritual of earning a good harvest as a blessing from God in return for leading good Christian lives. That the Church Christianised the broom indicates how important it had been – important spiritually because it was at Whitsun that people decorated their houses with it and that must have been a test of their faith in itself, believing that the protective power of a belief in Jesus Christ would overcome all other forces. Christianity brought to the fore the concept of humility and the broom became symbolic of that, from East Anglia to Devon, but why this should be so is not clear. The usual explanation relates to the Arrest of Jesus by the Roman guards who were able to approach him under cover of the noise of the wind in the broom branches in the Garden of Gethsemane. For this he reproached them.[11] An alternative story has the Virgin Mary, during the Flight into Egypt, worrying that as they pushed through the broom bushes the noise of the exploding seed pods would alert the soldiers to their position. I don't find either story very convincing in relation to such an important Christian concept as humility. Interestingly, visual renderings of the broom are very rare in medieval church art, as though humility came to the fore with Protestant preaching; certainly it was popular with the Puritans and again with the Victorians. The scriptures from which they preached humility are more likely to have been Psalm 120 and Job 30: 4-8. In these the 'juniper' of the King James Bible is now believed to be the White Broom, *Retama raetam*, common in desert wastes of Israel and Syria. References to eating the roots are believed to relate to the eating a parasite of the shrub, rather than the shrub itself.

In medieval art broom is most likely to be found as the emblem of the Royal House of Plantagent and can be found carved on royal tombs in Westminster Abbey etc. There are varying traditions as to how this started, featuring members of the House of Anjou, from which England got its King Henry II, the first Plantagenet king. He took that name from 'planta genista' – the broom. His son, King Richard I, put it on the Great Seal of England.

14

THE
SHRUBS AND
THEIR LANDSCAPE

Early man who created the folklore encountered these shrubs in very specific landscapes. In particular, as man and his livestock thinned the tree cover they would have broom among the pioneer plants in the new sunny areas. Broom still likes to grow along the sunny sides of woodlands, where it is happy with the humus-rich topsoil, relying on its own leguminous system of food production once the humic acid had been leached out. It prefers the deeper soil too and becomes scarce or absent out on shallow heathland soil. It would have been found more abundantly in the combes, benefiting from the run-off off water and nutrients and a build-up of deeper soil. Similarly it would have grown in the better soils along the fringe areas but these have so often been the very ones taken into cultivation and also on to which urban development has spread, depriving the shrub of its preferred habitat. Consequently we now see so little of it that we wonder how it could ever have been a plant of such economic importance. It was gorse rather than broom that benefited from clearances in open areas that became true heathland. These are always associated with acid soils but the broom tolerates calcium up to a reading of 6.5 on the pH scale and gorse is even more tolerant and will grow on lightly calcareous soils. It is very adept at absorbing all the calcium its roots can find and therefore it increases the acidity of the growing area and hastens the development of heathland. The practice of marling the fields encouraged both gorse and broom to flourish around the margins and it looks from the records as though this suited broom particularly

15

well. Not only calcium but other nutrients are scavenged by gorse roots and so it reduces the general nutrient level. It does make nutritious compost though! People added gorse clippings to seed drills to try and deter mice and birds from taking the seeds but they fertilized the seeds accidentally at the same time. Similarly, when livestock that had been fed gorse were put out on the heath they left behind good quality dung. All in all these shrubs would have accompanied increasing agricultural practice and maybe it was this that established the link with fertility rituals.

Being so adept at finding and storing soil nutrients is only part of their success story. They would not get enough nitrogen but that is overcome by them being 'leguminous', meaning they grow little nodules on their roots which house colonies of bacteria that take nitrogen gas out of the air and convert it to solid nitrogen compounds to feed the plant. This works so well that the shrubs can even grow in builders' rubble. A supreme demonstration of this in action occurred beside the Wey Navigation at Farncombe in Surrey. Land was bought with a view to building on it and to that end it was covered many feet deep with builders' rubble to raise it above the flood level. Then the prospective developer got strangled with the Green Belt red tape and building was not sanctioned, leaving a desert of totally infertile rubble. The first colonists were gorse and broom which covered in completely (magnificent in flower) through the feeding action of their root bacteria. After some ten years the litter layer and bacterial action had created enough food in the soil for two more colonists to move in, which were the dog rose and creeping thistle. The next year nettles and grasses joined them. Now, after nearly thirty years, the competitors are taking over and the landscape is clothed much as the rest of the Wey valley. Only one broom bush survives. The gorse has passed maturity and is losing vigour. Soon there will be no indication that this was once a man-made heathland.

Nutrition is not the only problem for heathland plants. Water is crucial. Either it lies in acid boggy pools over 'iron pans' and in effect drowns the vegetation unless specially adapted or else it drains away through the sand and down the gradients so fast that it soon leaves drought conditions behind. The gorse and broom have adapted to this by not having broad leaves. It is through the undersurfaces of these that other plants lose moisture through transpiration. With gorse and broom leaves are grown only in the very young stages and then production ceases; in the case of gorse, it produces leaves modified into spines. It is the green chlorophyll in the stems and spines takes over food production, with the advantage that these growths have far fewer breathing holes (stomata) through which the shrubs lose water during transpiration. Furthermore the green stems and spines are permanent, turning the shrubs into 'evergreens' and so food production can be continuous, so long as the light intensity is high enough to facilitate photosynthesis. There's even another advantage. Shrubs, that have evergreen *leaves* continue to have water sucked out of them by cold winter winds but if the ground water is frozen their roots are unable to draw up replacement water and the shrubs die of dehydration. Gorse and broom avoid that risk; when there's insufficient water they close their stomata and sit it out. They do the same thing in summer, when other plants would die of drought. Furthermore, not having heads of foliage to grow and feed reduces their need for food and so the poor soils are less of a problem than they are for most other plants.

How superbly these two shrubs have adapted. They do have a weakness though. They are not highly resistant to extreme cold. A hard frost kills the seedlings of broom and old mature specimens that are losing vigour. Extreme cold will cut back gorse severely. The warming influence over Britain from the North Atlantic has enabled these shrubs to flourish. If climate change brings harder, more continental style, winters the situation could change. That said, Britain has been through phases of savage winters before and the shrubs came through.

Not having to replace a great head of leaves each year means they put their energies into mass flowering and seed production. Each seed is large enough for us to handle individually, simply because each has been given a large amount of food reserves to get the seedling off to a good start in poor soil. Thus for over 4,000 years man has been able to incorporate these shrubs into his production cycles and build ways of life around them – as detailed in the following pages.

17

GRAZING AND FODDER

Origins

Wrapping up a culture in the name Neolithic and saying they were the first farmers, following on from hunters and gatherers, makes it sound so clear-cut, so distinctive, so different. Indeed it was, but, it was a gradual process. It took generations. People did not give up hunting and gathering overnight. Only gradually did the use of the land change, as man became more interested in increasing grazing, to attract the wild herbivores that could be killed for meat and leather etc. Ultimately they were herding these animals, developing their own semi-domesticated livestock, especially sheep, so that Bronze Age England had great sheep-runs. There were cattle too and by the Iron Age large cattle ranches had been established. Alongside this was the slow adoption of growing food crops. There was a lot to learn since managing livestock can be a nomadic business whereas crops do not go on the move. Thus settled communities came into being.[12] If they were also raising livestock it was essential that enough grazing was available within reach throughout the year. Grass browns off during a summer drought while winter frosts stop it growing but shrubs like heather and gorse can be grazed throughout the year. They did not need deliberate

18

cropping since they were colonising abandoned arable land, left by those early farmers who found they were soon exhausting the nutrient levels in their fields and moved on to create new ones. The bare disturbed soils of the abandoned fields were ideal seedbeds for the heather, gorse and broom and so heathlands became a significant part of the landscape.[13]

Gorse growing naturally

Early farmers found that gorse coppices very well. If their livestock nipped out the growing points the remaining stem would 'break' – burst into side shoots. Regular nibbling produced rounded hummocks, covered all over with a soft new browse. As this browse remained soft and spineless for several inches a great deal of browse could be produced. Ling breaks as well (unless eaten back to the hard wood) and so the two dominant heathland shrubs provided copious grazing. Ultimately it covered thousands of square miles of southern England.

Furze had other values apart from yielding browse and these will be reviewed shortly but for the moment, suffice to say it was so valuable that it was treated with respect and managed as a renewable resource. That gave rise to established practices, rights and customs that were administered and defended through the manorial courts, right up to the Enclosure Acts. In a few places Commoners' Rights are still extant and can involve gorse. Back in the medieval times we can guess how important shrub-fodder was to the heathland communities from the millions of sheep they were able to raise for England's famous woollen industry. Unfortunately the detail is often missing from surviving manorial records because heathland management was so often recorded as part of the manorial 'waste' and that included non-heathland areas too. The word has changed its meaning. The manorial *waste* was the *unploughed* land that was not woodland. It was not wasteland in the modern sense at all. Far from it; heathlands were a valuable asset to any manor, enabling greater densities of livestock to be raised and extending the range of raw materials available.[14] Sometimes our ancestors did see this as a separate resource and so, for example, a description of the Manor of Eastbury, at Compton, Surrey, in 1572 includes 40 acres of furze and heath separately from the 'waste'.[15]

19

The fact that these shrubs – heather, gorse and broom – were used for grazing at all surprises some people. Surely livestock are supposed to be in fields eating grass! Well that's a modern view. In the past people exploited *all* the resources of their manor and those resources were limited. The prime limitation so often gets overlooked and that was the boundary. Each community had a limited area of land that comprised their manor and it was from within that boundary that they needed to sustain themselves. If they could produce a surplus of anything for trade so much the better. Even where they did have enough grassy pasture they had to remove their livestock from it in late spring and early summer so that the grasses and other plants could grow up into the flowering stage ready for hay-making. Without hay there was no other winter feed for the livestock, until the 17th century introduction of turnips into the cropping rotation. Even that idea took two hundred years to spread in practice from S. E. England as far north as the Lake District. Removing the livestock posed the two-fold problem of where to put them and upon what to feed them, but areas of heathland solved that promptly with its predominance of heather. As far as we know gorse was usually mixed in and played only a small part but on small heathlands every little helped.

How much grass was growing on the heathlands is arguable. The National Trust on their Witley Common site in Surrey have been cutting the heather to try and encourage it to thicken it up and that is exactly what has happened. The bracken is retreating and the thicker heather is overwhelming grasses and other plants. Presumably this was the structure of English heathlands when they had millions of sheep browsing them. Nearby, on part of Hindhead Common, the National Trust has reintroduced grazing with cattle and ponies, in the hope of reclaiming heathland from bracken invasion. The site chosen was known to me as a child as a complete swathe of bracken that was not pleasant or easy to walk across at any season. Now the livestock have reduced it dramatically and the new landscape is a varied patchwork of heather and gorse, birch and willow and brambles, with some bracken, all broken up with grassy areas and grassy walkways. It's not very good grass from a farming viewpoint but nevertheless there is grass. That sort of landscape is what many people think the heathlands looked like centuries ago. I do not agree entirely. I think it arises from the low density of animals kept on it. In the past the stocking was high density. I think grasses would, on the whole, have been grazed out. When they shoot up to flowers they have their highest concentrations of sugars and the cattle would have stripped them off, removing the seeding potential. That arose out of cattle having teeth in only one jaw and so they wrap their tongues round the grasses and sever them against the cutting edge of the teeth – hence that wonderful tearing noise of cattle grazing. Sheep have the same problem but solve it by clamping the grass with one jaw against the teeth of the other and then jerking the head to sever the stems. That would yank grass seedlings out of the ground. I'm not of the opinion that there was a significant amount of grass on heathlands in the past, certainly not in the Middle Ages before the wool industry declined in most of the south. With the economic changes came the age of agricultural 'Improvements' and then gorse got a new lease of life.

Ulex in.
R McG

21

Gorse as a crop

People knew full well that it was important on the heathlands for grazing and that it improved the soil so they started growing it with the corn. The seed was mixed and sown together. The gorse was still soft and spineless at the time of the corn harvest and so was not cursed by the reapers. We read again and again that after the harvest the livestock were turned into the fields to '*eat the stubble.*' No they were not. Stubble is straw. It's practically tasteless and has so little nutritive value it cannot sustain the animals. What they ate were the green weeds and any undercrop that had been sown with the corn (particularly if it was oats and barley). That undercrop was usually of leguminous plants, primarily the clovers and trefoils, but also gorse. They are dark green plants, full of nitrogen compounds (from their root nodules of bacteria) that are the basis of protein and make good fodder. The nitrogenous nodules put fertility into the soil when the land was ploughed again after the livestock had grazed off the greenery. While they were grazing they dunged the land which aided fertility by recycling the nutrients. Similarly, seed of gorse and the other legumes was mixed with grass seed when a pasture was being sown afresh. Fortunately the gorse was still soft when the mowers took off the first hay harvest!

Seed supplies and sowing

It is so easy to say that gorse seed was sown but behind that statement lies the activity of the farming family collecting their own from the hard black seed pods and they had to collect thousands of them at that. Otherwise they had to buy it. The idea of buying seeds sounds familiar enough today but at some unknown date in history (almost certainly in the 17th century) gorse seed must have come on to the market for the first time, signifying not simply a demand but one great enough to finance the collection of the seed and its retailing. It is one of those topics from our English social history that is practically unknown. Certainly seed merchants were in existence in the 17th century and some offered gorse, such as William Lucas at his shop with the sign of The Naked Boy or The Three Naked Boys, in the Strand, London, in 1677.[16] We are left to imagine the harvesting, presumably by women and children, who would have been paid but a few pennies for hours and hours spent on the finger

22

stabbing job of collecting the seed pods. How the seeds were released seems to have gone unrecorded. Possibly the pods were pounded in a linen bag or, more likely, the bag was left in the sun to make the ripe pods explode in the usual way. Alternatively podded branches may have been cut and left to shed their seeds, on to cloths or in bags, before the branches were used or sold on as fuel. These are the people, tasks and techniques that have escaped documentation, leaving us to deduce their former existence. The extent of local trade is unknown, but gorse seed could be bought in large quantities. Think how many pods would need to burst to shed a bushel of seed and yet farmers were instructed to sow it at the rate of 40 lb to the acre if it was for fodder: *"the plant does not branch, it throws up straight, long, succulent shoots from the roots, with few or no spines along the stem, presenting no difficulty to the scythe in mowing it down. Seed should be sown in May, at the latest, and at the rate of 40lb to the statute and 65lb to the Irish acres"*[17] If harvesting was left to the following year the crop could have been sold as fuel.

An alternative to broadcast sowing was to sow in rows, either to create a hedge or a hedge-like crop in open ground. As an alternative to sowing in drills there was the rope method of great antiquity. It was described by the ancient Greek writer, Democritus, and that was copied in 1677 by Thomas Hill for *The Gardener's Labyrinth* (the first popular gardening book in English) wherein he instructs upon the collection of fruits and seeds for making a mixed hedge and decrees, *"mix and steep for a time, all the berries and seeds in the binding meale of Tares, unto the thickness of honey: the same mixture lay diligently into old and untwisted Ship or Wel-ropes, or other long worne ropes, and fittered or broken into short pieces, being in the manner starke rotten, in such order, that the seeds bestowed or couched within the soft haires of them, may be preserved and defended from the cold, unto the beginning of spring."* Then, he explains, the rope should be unrolled into a drill along the route of the proposed hedge, covered lightly with soil and watered if necessary. This same principle, but adjusted specifically for gorse, was recorded from Ireland by A.T. Lucas. The main difference was that in Ireland the rope was made specifically for gorse, from hay or straw, and soaked in horse manure to give it nutrients to foster the

23

seedlings; the rope itself would have added organic matter and retained moisture. The practice was developed sufficiently for such ropes to acquire their own name, 'súgán', and to be twisted by a special tool, also with its own name. 'crúicin'. The seeds were inserted 18ins apart and the rope rolled out into a channel etc. in the ancient Greek method. It's difficult to imagine that all this was worth the effort but evidently it was. Inevitably there were those who simply ploughed or dug a channel and sowed the seeds direct, brushing in bonfire ashes as a potash fertilizer (using a gorse branch as the brush of course) and then harrowing the soil over the top, with gorse branches.

Sowing by rope was most likely to have been for boundary hedges although of course they had the added benefit that when trimmed the clippings could be fed to the livestock. Drilling across the land was for cropping, for fodder and fuel, and the rows were spaced widely so as to leave enough space between for other crops or for pasture. By moving the gorse strips across the field each time, the farmers replaced nitrogen into the soil. This was known as giving a '*furze break*'. Our ancestors really knew how to get the best return from their limited land. They chose their best options and so it is important to remember that the material presented in this book will not apply to *all* manors and heathlands at *all* times. For example, I have no record for the deliberate cultivation of gorse from the New Forest and its environs, leaving us to presume there was enough growing wild to satisfy local demand.

Gorse fodder

Cutting gorse to deliver to animals as fodder, centres upon horses, which love it and will turn away from hay to eat it first. Cattle are not so partial to it when they are fed it chopped coarsely but if it is mashed they eat it well enough. In districts away from the southern heaths, in Wales, Scotland and Ireland, it was much used for the cattle. It is sheep that are the most reluctant to relish it as a feed supplement but out on the

pastures sheep do graze it, especially in very cold weather – you can see little beads of blood on their muzzles caused by the spines. They are much happier with the soft young growth and so after coppicing the stools the yield was, in some regions, scythed off for the sheep, before it got much beyond a year old. In late times, with the increase in the numbers of urban horses feed had to be bought in and gorse played its part there too. The problem was all those spines. Ideally young growth was used when it was spineless or while still soft, otherwise the spines had to be crushed. That's simple to say but hard to do, especially when so much was needed. Just as the size and appetite of a horse varied so did the generosity of the owner! Sometimes the quantity was reduced by adding oats or other feed. Gorse has about half the protein content of oats and therefore makes good fodder from a nutritive viewpoint. In Ireland a pannier per horse per day is recorded, with a pannier holding 21lbs. More frequent estimates range between 25-30lbs, qualified as being for a small horse. People who could afford big horses could probably afford to buy in better feed.

At its simplest the spines were dealt with by crushing – by pounding the cuttings on a stone with a wooden mallet or else in a wooden trough with a stone. It was never stone against stone or wood against wood. The Irish evolved special long-handled mallets,

up to four feet long for a good swing, with tapering circular heads, bound in iron. These had two cross blades set in the wider end, projecting beyond the head. There were also versions with iron studs in the end. Either way it was obviously hard work as it took a day to pound enough for a horse team but again records range widely, from four to eight horses, and depending on whether the gorse was already cut and to hand. For cattle it had to be pulped extra soft. In Scotland they flailed it, which is not very effective, so the flails were bladed with pieces of hoop iron. It's hardly surprising that many farmers put it through the cider mill while in other places the usage was sufficient to warrant the building of special water mills, wherein wooden mallets pounded the stuff (Isle of Man) or toothed rollers tore it apart (Wales). A mill from Dolwen, Clwyd has been rebuilt at the Welsh Folk Museum, at St Fagans, near Cardiff. Such mills became well established by c.1800 only to be superseded by hand machines as 19th century inventiveness got under way. Some correspondents remembered putting it through the chaff-cutter and old farming catalogues show the chaff cutter design as a gorse cutter. In the old records preparing the fodder is often called 'bruising' which implies that hand crushing was the first technique and that chopping, tearing, etc. evolved out of it. However, wording varies according to the local dialect, so it is to 'cree' with a 'mell' in the *Memoirs* of the artist Thomas Bewick, (born in 1753 at Ovingham, Tyneside): *"In the early spring it was a common job for me before setting off to school to rise betimes in the morning, and eqipt with an apron, an old dyking mitten and a sharpened broken sickle to set off among the whin bushes, which were near to hand to cut off last year's sprouts. These were laid in a corner until the evening when I stript and fell to work to 'cree' them with a 'mell' in a stone trough till the tops of the whins were beaten to the consistency of soft, wet grass and with this mess I fed the*

26

horses before I went to bed. It agreed so well with them with a little oats that they soon became sleek." It was a daily task because the gorse had to be used fresh, otherwise it would start to ferment. Recently, in Scotland, there have been investigations into re-introducing this product for local consumption.[18]

The notion of the sleek coat is reported far and wide, for over three centuries: *"The young and tender Tops of Furzes, being a little bruised, and given to a lean, sickly Horse, will strangely recover and plump him."*[19] Similarly, reports today uphold the claim that a sickly horse fed on such tops recovers quickly. A horse off its feed can be enticed with a bundle of uncrushed gorse hung up in the stall to be nibbled. People still hang up gorse in the winter stall for the horse to nibble because the spines make it a slow and careful nibble which concentrates the mind and relieves the horse from boredom problems. The remaining sticks, stripped of their bark, were used up as domestic fuel. Another old notion, still upheld, says horses fed on uncrushed gorse over a length of time grow a protective moustache in defence against the sharp spines. Others assert that horses grow moustaches when kept in stalls through the winter and lose them as soon as they return to grazing, as in this early 20th century remembrance of Enstone, Oxon.: *"Most of 'em growed a moustache while they were feeding indoors for the winter, but it soon wore off once they were out at pasture, grazing again, in the spring."*[20]

All this tradition with horses implies that there must have been extensive areas of gorse specifically for fodder. Just think how many acres would be needed for one team of horses needing 30lb a day per horse! That said, these records are from the later period. Earlier, the counties with a lot of heathland, such as Surrey, simply did not have many horses. Oxen ploughed the land. Henry VII passed an Act requiring the breeding of more horses[21] but this was obviously not implemented in any lasting way seeing as Elizabeth I had the same problem. Whenever she wanted to travel through Surrey the county had to provide the horses and they could never find enough. They hired extras from over the Thames in Middlesex and then passed on the charge to her. She was furious: *"Henceforth all my good people in the County of Surrey with a park more than one mile in circumference must breed more brood mares."* There were only about thirty six such estates so that law was not likely to solve the problem and even by the time of the Civil Wars the troops moving through the county could not muster enough hay and oats for their horses[22] which may indicate low numbers but there are other implications, of course, in a military situation. Similarly uncertain are the high-value references put upon gorse in the 19th century which have been interpreted as for fuel, as will be explored later, but some of this production might have been for fodder.

Certainly, in heathland districts where they worked gorse the stockman would always have had a supply of gorse fodder to hand. This was so important in the late winter when hay supplies could be dwindling and cold March winds would retard the spring re-growth of soft herbaceous fodder. Using evergreen trees and shrubs, suchas holly and ivy, had its problems since the native ones are defended with toxins.[23] Gorse was always considered safe because its level of toxins is so low. By continually cutting it they revitalised it and a stool will continue to re-sprout almost indefinitely whereas a shrub left uncut reaches full maturity in about thirty years and then goes into terminal decline. Regular harvesting of this renewable resource meant also that it was still at a manageable size and not impenetrable thickets over head high. At that height they are also suppressing the adjacent ground flora which would otherwise have provided more fodder. Careful management made gorse a highly profitable resource and one that enriched the soil so that traditional lore asserts:

Where there's bracken there's gold.
Where there's furze there's silver.
Where there's heather there's poverty.

Gold under furze.
Silver under rushes.
Famine under heath.

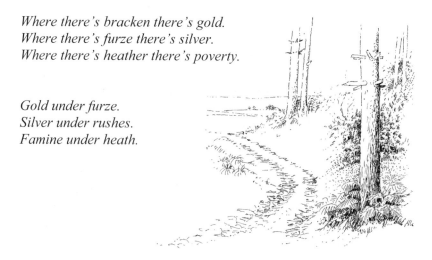

Broom

Broom as fodder has only a limited recorded history so it is difficult to assess its importance; our ancestors did not make many records of the commonplace. We can be certain that it was *not* managed in the same way as gorse because of the nature of the plant. Chop broom back into the hard wood and it dies. It simply will not coppice like gorse. Even cutting the green young growth requires caution because about a third of that potential must be left; else the shrub does not re-sprout. Thus it would seem to be of limited value in this capacity but if it is all that the stockman had in times of need then it was invaluable.

Farmers learned that allowing sheep to over-indulge resulted in 'drunkenness' from the compounds therein but farming lore also decreed that allowing sheep to nibble broom saves them from diseases like dropsy and the rot. John Aubrey (1685)[24] said he knew of farmers who had destroyed their broom only to have their sheep attacked by rot and *"so ever since they doe leave a border of broom around their grounds for their sheep to browse on, to keep them sound."* This makes it sound like an arable weed around the margins of the field and that would make sense when seed was sown broadcast and the wind could carry it astray. It was sown with the corn to provide fodder after the harvest as described already for gorse. Was it perhaps sown as a crop in its own right while a field was fallow? It would enrich the soil, being leguminous like gorse, and provide fodder or broom-making material in the winter, before a late ploughing ready for spring-sown crops. That might help explain why so many estate maps with the field names marked on them have one named 'broom field'. What did this mean? Was broom the crop or was it heather for making brooms, or even a birch or sycamore coppice for the broom-handles? We don't know. Different farms would have different understandings. Normally fields were not named after a one-season crop so in all likelihood the designation 'broom field' was of a semi-permanent nature. Maybe it had sheep-grazing between the shrubs from time to time, with a strip of spent shrubs ploughed out every now and again to encourage fresh seedlings, in much the same way as a 'furze break'. Broom germinates readily in disturbed soil, as after turf-cutting, and so would have responded positively to the working of the heathlands.

29

In fact it likes loose soil so that it can run out long roots and for this reason has been much used for stabilising sand dunes. The roots soon mat together and stabilise the ground (the French have exploited this more than the British). It also regenerates well in bare ground after fire.

GORSE FOR FUEL

Gorse burns with great heat. It has one of the highest calorific values of any fuel available to our ancestors[25] and for this reason was cropped specifically as a fuel, in three categories: green growth fresh, green growth dried and the woody stems.

Gathering gorse for fuel became known as 'faggoting' and that dates back to the Middle Ages. The term (derived ultimately from the Greek for bundle) came to England from the French, suggesting this may date from the early Middle Ages when Norman French was the language of officialdom. Before that things are more hazy. In the local dialect of counties such as Hampshire the term 'smutting' occurs, linking with sootiness and fires. Those readers brought up in the days of open fires will no doubt remember their mothers remonstrating against flying smuts – they did not dust off but smeared. The word derives from the Saxon *smitt* meaning to smear. Thus dialects have 'black smutting' and 'white smutting'. The latter is the clean green harvest while the former related to harvesting the blackened branches left after a fire, which blacken the hands, clothes and everything else. Today we can be all too familiar with gaunt blackened gorse stems after a heathland fire and conservationists are keen to know whether our ancestors fired the heaths at regular intervals as per the 'swaling' of heather of the Pennine grouse moors etc. That will be discussed later but at this point let us note that the Saxon language hints at a familiarity with burnt gorse bushes. Although that is tenuous there is another connection to back it up. The burnt stools left after a fire are known in dialects as 'moots' and it is said that the origin of this is unknown. Well here is a suggestion. The gorse reserves belonged to the community and were regulated through the manorial courts to maintain them fairly as a renewable resource. Once the top growth had been burnt off, who in the community should benefit from the valuable fuel of the surviving stools of stems? That would be debated in the Saxon 'moot courts'. A debatable point is still a 'moot point'. Through the courts the options for black and white smutting became part of 'commoners rights' in some places but not by those names in others.

31

Harvesting Gorse

Cutting gorse is a nightmare. Nevertheless the harvesting and selling of gorse became a specific occupation, for people known variously as a furzer, furze cutter, faggot cutter, faggoter, or something recognisably similar. Like any other occupation it developed its own techniques, tools, language, practices and rituals, which varied from district to district around the British Isles and so the following is a particularly generalised summary.

When gorse was cut on a regular basis there were three options practised regularly. Either it was cut when it was a year old and soft enough to cut easily, or in its second year when it was generally less than 18 inches high or in the third year when it was getting woody. The three year rotation provided a good and economic return and was widespread. Rev. H Townsend was expecting it to be left until the third year when he wrote: *"It may well be very well worth the farmer's pains to devote an acre or two to furze: after the third year's growth from seed it will afford an abundant annual cutting."*[26]

Young gorse yields to scythe and sickle while older gorse requires some form of billhook. Using sickles predates scythes and the best type of sickle was a traditional one with the cutting edge serrated. The best scythe was the modified 'furze scythe', which had its back strengthened at the time or forging (rather than having a strip riveted on afterwards) and it had a shorter blade than did a grass scythe. It was common practice to harvest gorse on a three year rotation and for this the billhook was needed. The second tool required was a stick with which to hold over the spiny stem. The sticks ranged from about 12-30 inches long and are recorded as T-shaped while other records are for Y-shaped sticks. The Y-shaped stick would have been the better option since they would prevent the stem slipping sideways and made a better rake for drawing up the cuttings. So the stem was held with the stick in one hand while the other swiped it off with a bill-hook. Huh! You try it! The stem is incredibly hard and fibrous even though it is still relatively thin and looks as though it would yield to a single blow. Get the angle wrong and the blade glances along the stem, slicing through bark and twigs but leaving the main stem intact. It is one of those simple-looking tasks that actually demands expertise – in pinning the stem over at the right angle to the cutter and then striking at the best angle.

32

Gorse-cutting: there was a variety of bill-hook designs in use. Some cutters could afford leather gaiters.

Alternatively, the growth was held down over the blade which was then drawn up to sever the stem. I found that method even more back-breaking than chopping. Either way, our ancestors must have worked their way over a crop at a very economic rate. That is how Thomas Hardy portrayed his character Clym Yeobright in *Return of the Native*: *"busily chopping away at the furze, a long row of faggots which stretched downward from his position representing the labour of the day."* Young soft and succulent gorse was best for fodder while ageing hardening stems were best for fuel.

Hardy described Yeobright in wondrous protective clothing which suggests the gorse was tall and mature but this was 1878 when the end of the tradition was approaching, in many regions. In earlier times the gorse would have been cut younger as described above, not only for the convenience but also to satisfy the greater need. Few villagers could have afforded the luxury of Yeobright's leather gloves and leather aprons etc. when harvesting was only periodic and relatively small scale. Then the community paid for communal gloves etc., as per the entry, *'Two pairs of gloves bought for the manor servants'* in the Court Rolls of Bramshott Manor (Hants) for the year 1412/13.[27] It does not say for what they were intended. Without gloves the cutters bound their hands with rags or wound rope round them. The rope technique persisted in Ireland until recent times. Once faggoting became a specialist occupation protective clothing became essential. Leather gloves were expensive and only one might be bought, or a cheaper mitten, for the left hand. The right hand has protected by the billhook having a wrist guard. The legs needed protection too and leather leggings were best, preferably reaching above the knee, but again these were expensive and a cutter might buy only one, for the left leg (all this presuming he was right-handed).

Making faggots

The cut stems were bundled and taken home for binding up into uniform faggots, leaving no useful trimmings to waste out in the countryside. Lucas published a description of the art of bundling:-

"A length of twine was stretched on the ground, one end being tied to a small stick stuck in the ground. The other end was tied in a groove near the lower end of a much longer stick, called a 'bock',

which was also stuck upright in the ground, so that the twine was held at full stretch. The furze sticks were then laid traversly across the string and packed up against the 'bock'. When enough had been heaped up to make a bundle of the proper size, the 'bock' was pulled up, bringing the end of the twine with it which was taken round the bundle and tied to the end attached to the small stick. "[28]

Instead of twine they used withes' made from willow shoots, or a long shoot or gorse itself was used, or barked bramble shoots. The last were sometimes called 'briars' but should not be confused with roses or heather. Hardy's Yeobright went *"in search of brambles for faggot-bonds."* Whether the faggots were made out in the countryside or at home they had to be of standard size and quality. So important was this product that towns and cities passed laws and regulations to govern and control size, quality and price. Bearing n mind that being a faggotter could be a full-time occupation then these regulations had a major impact upon local rural life and upon individual families if penalties were incurred. A good faggoter could cut and tie a hundred faggots a day and for a long time in recent history that day's work would have earned him 2/6d, whether in Ireland or Dorset. That was about one fifth of the top retail price of the hundred.

35

Obviously it was crucial that the faggots be well tied to withstand a journey to town and the tossing about as they were stacked. There was such an art to this that it became an additional skill to show off to the spectators at ploughing matches. The gorse, still with its heads of twiggy tops, was stacked in two bundles so that the heads were at either end and the main stems crossed in the centre. These were then tied with a figure of eight bond made from a long, young, shoot of gorse. There was a particularly clever knack of fixing one end into the other end so as to make the tie totally secure and capable of withstanding all the manhandling. Two year old gorse was highly prized for faggots so, if close-grown, the stems would not have made a particularly bushy head, nor would the stems have been so long as to pose problems.

Tightening faggots ready for binding was achieved by laying them over the binding and a cord with handles, which was then raised round them and pulled tight once the handles had been crossed over.

Town Markets

Today, when fuel comes instantly with the click of a switch, it is difficult to imagine the hundreds of faggots that would be needed every day by large towns and cities. They were needed as fuel for both domestic hearths and for industrial processing, such as baking, brewing and dyeing. They were preferred over alternative fuels because they burn with such intense heat.[29]

Experience soon taught our ancestors that large stacks of gorse were a serious fire risk. Not only were they highly inflammable but gave off such an intense heat that no one could have got close with pails of water to extinguish the fire. Consequently, in the days when towns protected themselves with walls, the regulations of the town councils insisted upon gorse stacks being outside those walls and forbade the storing of more than one day's supply within. Some processes, like bread-making, ran on a cycle that did not fit neatly the normal hours of fuel trading and so bakers flouted the regulations. So did brewers. Where preserved, it is the legal proceedings against them that give an insight into this aspect of former urban life. Thus we have to imagine the business centre for trading faggots being outside the walls, and presumably convenient to a gateway. Here we have to imagine the bustle as deliveries arrived, in carts and back-packs, and all the counting and checking for quality control before payment could be made. Prices were fixed so that should have reduced argument, unless a faggot was deemed undersized! We know from records that the officers measured them with metal hoops of the agreed standard size but trying to pass a faggot through one of these would have been difficult and wasted a lot of time, so Lucas suggested the hoop might have been split and hinged like a giant pair of callipers. To speed things up and save arguments the faggoters must surely have done their own measurements before leaving home, perhaps by wrapping a knotted cord round the bundle.

Another centre of activity, for some towns only, would be down at their waterfront if supplies arrived by boat. It occurred to Lucas that in Ireland they might have practised the expedient of roping the bundles together and rafting them to downstream destinations. Searches for parallel evidence from southern England have not been fruitful. However, in East Sussex there are manorial accounts for paying the harvesters out on the heathland and for dealing with the yield back at the home farm but no accounts at all for transport between the two. The two sites are linked by the River Adur.[30] Was the gorse rafted down? Rafting would require the bundles being left for a while to dry out and that would help explain the references to giant stacks. Otherwise the stacks were being created by the supply outstripping the demand and on this scale that notion calls attention to itself. Industrial needs were obviously continuous but so were domestic needs when all food was cooked over fires. Perhaps the giant stacks are due solely to people following the usual advice to cut the fuel in May and leave it there to dry till September and then gather it for use and trade. That would certainly create a seasonal influx during the autumn. However, it leaves us wondering whether thieves would leave such a valuable commodity lying around for four months and could the traders cope with the burden of this work in early autumn when there was so much else to do at that time in the agricultural calendar. Extra supplies were brought in during the winter months from cutting mature gorse. At present it is far from clear how this part of the economy worked but there are records to prove that gorse stacks really did exist and you only have to look on the street map of Chester to see they still have a road called 'Gorse Stacks' where fuel was stacked.

We can imagine streams of townsfolk, especially apprentices, in the early morning light, pouring through the gateway to get their daily fuel before work could begin. Fresh deliveries gave rise to new stacks and what great stacks they must have been too, since they rose higher than the city walls, causing alarm that 'enemies' could use them to get over the walls. The use of 'enemies' might well be a euphemism for cheats trying to avoid paying tolls at the gateways. The height of stacks was soon regulated to a number of feet below the height of the wall. Stacking was the work of two men: the 'pikeman' on the ground who pitched up the faggots with a dung fork and the 'stacker' on top who built up and shaped the stack with a hay fork. While all this was going on other stacks were being dismantled to meet the day's demand. They must have been wonderful habitats for rats and so we should probably imagine the rat-catchers and their terriers poised in lethal readiness for the rats' final dash. In all probability purchasers at the stacks had the choice of two different fuels: the mature woody stems or young spiny growth. Carrying off spiny gorse through narrow crowded streets sounds fraught with hazard for the other people! Was there a special 'street cry' to warn them aside?

Fuel for bakers

Producing bread was a slow process because of the time needed for the dough to prove and so the full cycle could take sixteen hours. Bakers therefore wanted a fuel that would heat their ovens very hotly very quickly and to these ends gorse was supreme. Furthermore, it burns down to very little ash which was important because it was fired in the bottom of the oven itself (until c.1835 onwards) where the dough needed to be placed. Dough was not in tins so the ash and any chips of charcoal would stick in the bread crust. Consequently ovens had to be swept out immediately prior to inserting the dough and this had to be done fast, so as not to lose valuable heat, but vigour could bring disaster. If a flying piece of burning charcoal landed in the fuel heap the whole bakehouse could be consumed in fire before people had chance to quench it. Remember, the Great Fire of London started in a bakehouse in Pudding Lane. From contemporary descriptions we know that a second hazard came into play. Gorse is rich in oils and when heated this oil vaporises and hangs as a shimmering cloud over the fire, absorbing more heat until it bursts into a fireball. That is what happened on that day in 1666. A calmer but slower way of cleaning the oven floor was to roll a 'sausage' of dough over it so that the ash and charcoal stuck to it. That dough roll was known as 'cake' which puts a whole new complexions upon that famous remark attributed to Marie Antoinette that the Parisians, starving for want of bread, should eat cake. Today cake has currants instead of charcoal! Things clogged with debris, usually muddy boots, are still described as 'caked-up'.

39

The demand for fuel from bakers would not have been as great as might be imagined. It was not every community that had a *public bakehouse*. It was considered the hallmark of a good housewife to be able to bake her own bread and good bread at that. There was prejudice against 'shop bread', so that even today in Lancashire it is remembered that anyone talking rubbish was 'talking off his shop loaf'. Public bakehouses were a town feature because it was there that families were too busy plying their other skills to stop and bake their own bread. The demand for fuel for ovens is difficult to appreciate today, not knowing the size of the oven or of the faggots, but accounts regularly quote 2-7 faggots per firing. When accounts increase up to 30 it must surely be a public bakehouse, especially as that much fuel could cost three shillings or more. Large ovens were hot enough when the bricks began to whiten with the heat, otherwise they were tested by throwing flour on the oven floor - if it blackened it was hot enough but if it burst into flames it was too hot. No wonder baking was such an art!

For generations the furze-cutters could sell the tops to the bread bakers and the older stems to the brick and tile bakers. Thus they were able to balance supply and demand but by the 19th century the building boom meant the latter could afford higher prices and so the bakers lost out. The answer was to grow gorse as a crop specially for the bakers. Thus in 1862 Johnson reported,

"In Surrey, and other counties around the metropolis, large quantities are consumed by the bakers for heating ovens. On some of the sandy districts of western Surrey it is sown for this purpose, being ready to cut about three years after sowing, and yielding a crop of faggots at similar intervals for several years."[31]

This is borne out by property sales particulars in the area, such as for Potters Park Farm (Chobham and Chertsey parishes) in 1817 which listed:-

Copse and Furze Field of 4 acres 2 rods 29 perches
New Furze Field of 8 acres 9 perches
Lower Furze Field of 16 acres 3 rods 26 perches[32]

Another document in the same archive relates to Halwick Manor Farm between Chertsey and Byfleet when sold in 1817:

Furze field – 4 acres 3 rods 32 perches
Plus furze – 1 acre 3 rods 23 perches

A mile away is Ottershaw Park, for which a 1722 mortgage agreement lists "*160 acres of furze and heath, now unfenced*"[33] Having fields of Furze was obviously a sound investment and 'Furze Field' occurs widely on local maps around the British Isles, plus variants such as 'Gossners' at Laleham, Middlesex. There's Furzen Farm at Alfold, Surrey, and less obvious from the same village, Figbush Farm which in 1558 was spelt Fykbush, meaning pointed, as in thorns, and could well refer to Furze. Not far off, at Cranleigh, is Freeswell which used to be spelt Furzehill and before that, in 1294, was Furshall.[34]

Not all cooking was done in the oven. The famous Irish griddle bread was 'toasted' in front of the fire and there are variants upon that idea from Scotland, Wales, etc. Furze as a domestic fuel was especially valuable for the speedy rekindling of the hearth in the mornings or when returning from the fields, and to bring pots and kettles to the boil. In these cases it was known as a 'hurrier'.

Devil's Punch Bowl, Surrey

41

Lime kilns

Lime-burners made an important demand for gorse fuel, even if only for a couple of centuries. It had long been known that fertility could be increased by marling – spreading calcareous clay on the fields. Then it was found more effective to burn calcareous rock (chalk and limestones) to make lime and to spread that on the fields. The acidic soils of the south are often within carting distance of the chalk downs, with market towns in the river gaps, so

Derelict Lime Kiln

there developed the practice of bringing back chalk blocks in the empty carts after going to market, as recorded by Gertrude Jekyll:-

"Farms throughout the district [Godalming, Surrey] *had their own kilns for burning the lime. Many of these kilns have been destroyed, but a fair number remain. They were built in steeply sloping ground by or near a roadside, where the loads of chalk could be drawn up to their top level. The larger blocks of chalk were built up inside the kiln (which is circular in plan and open at the top), in the form of a rough arch, corresponding more or less to the opening, and the smaller pieces of chalk were filled in above. The space underneath was filled with furze faggots, and a certain amount of burning converted the chalk to lime."* [35]

Although she says these were circular in plan that applies usually to the interior only; the outside was recurrently square. As for being open at the top, that was only until the kiln was filled with its layers of chalk or lime and fuel, after which it was sealed over with a dome of soil, leaving a central chimney type air vent. After firing and cooling the remaining mixture of soil from the dome, fuel ashes, and lime, was raked out through the basal apertures. This was 'quicklime' (calcium oxide) which is dangerously caustic until it has been doused with water to convert it to 'slaked lime' (calcium hydroxide). If it was not needed at once it could be stacked in the open to convert naturally in the rainfall. Obviously these kilns could consume vast amounts of gorse, especially in those years of the 19th century when corn harvests were poor, prices soared, people starved and there was every incentive to increase the productivity of the land. There was also a great demand for lime for the building boom. With that in mind, my attention has been drawn[36] to the word *pye*. It is suggested that this was a fuel for limekilns made from mixing bracken with gorse, and as such gave rise to place names in North East Hampshire, along the route of the Basingstoke Canal. If *pye* was this fuel, were the locations along the canal for ease of transport or from making the lime needed for the mortar for building the locks? The latter would explain the impermanence of the sites since only one has prospered, Pyestock, now a suburb of Farnborough. For that a kiln site has been identified and located, complete with well for slaking the lime but those are not conclusive evidence for the derivation.

End of the Fuel Tradition

Back in the 17th century John Evelyn had written that nothing was "more excellent" than furze fuel and so it remained in use until the end of the 19th century for the poorer peoples of the heathlands. By then however the bustling stack yards outside the city walls had been long forgotten. Coal had taken over, both for domestic and industrial uses, and was widely available, courtesy of the Victorians' enthusiasm for railways. In the meantime the open countryside had been 'Inclosed' and many rural communities lost their common land and their commoners' rites. The right to take fuel was usually included as part of people's 'right of estovers', from the Latin *est opus*, meaning *it is necessary* and fuel was certainly necessary. Consequently many rural employers had to start providing fuel for their workers, as part of their wages. The canal owners developed this at an early date for their lock keepers, to reduce the risk of them leaving their posts to go 'shopping' or to steal a scoop of coal off the back of a barge. Similarly the owners of country estates provided fuel for their head gardeners, gamekeepers etc. as part of their wages. The alternative was for a provision of land to be set-aside for the

43

benefit of the poor. Thus at Sunbury-on-Thames the Inclosures created a new *'Fuel Land Estate'* charity: *"for the benefit of the poor of the parish of Sunbury in lieu of and in full compensation and satisfaction for all and every right or rights which was or were or might be or have been claimed by the poor of the same parish of cutting furze, heath and turf on the waste lands and grounds for fuel."*

From the same Middlesex parish it was proposed in the following year, 1801, that the inmates of the workhouse should be employed cutting furze.[37] They were supposed to be usefully employed.

While coal reduced demand from some potential markets others developed and such was the case with the brickyards. Many a village had one since Tudor times or soon afterwards and flourished when the Georgians made brick highly fashionable, to be followed by the 19th century building boom. This was especially noticeable as the railways brought development to the last remaining wildernesses – the heathlands and many a town has an interesting story on that subject, e.g. Woking, Camberley and Frimley, Surrey. Thornton Heath became a residential area of Croydon. Cradley Heath became an industrial area in the West Midlands. Part of the notorious Hounslow Heath was taken over for Heathrow Airport. The development on a hitherto unknown scale caused alarm with some people of which the most famous result was the founding of the National Trust.

Broom for fuel

Broom charcoal has been found in a Mesolithic site well over 6,000 years old which may indicate the discovery that the dead twigs ignite readily and make excellent kindling material. The thicker stems burn well too with a good heat. Being a short-lived shrub there must have been plenty of dead ones to use. This must have persisted down the ages for in the 17th century John Evelyn commented that to burn broom took the pressure off other fuels. People would also have burned their broom besoms when they hardened too much for sweeping.

44

HEALTH CARE
Gorse

The nutritive value of gorse for livestock is limited but in poor heathland communities it saved lives. This was particularly true in Ireland following the Potato Famine when root crops and hay were scarce and highly priced. For human health, gorse has not played a great part. Decoctions of the growth are astringent and have been used against diarrhoea and what Gerard called *"for staying of the laske"* which the dictionary defines as *"laxness of the bowels"*. It was used also for excessive menstrual flow and for various stones. The yellow flowers suggested it would cure yellow jaundice, which treatment derives from the Doctrine of Signatures. It was better for worms and is still in country remedies today. A handful of the flowers were boiled, sometimes in milk, strained, and the fluid administered. This was considered mild enough for use on children but readers should consult a qualified herbalist before experimenting. Animals on the other hand were kept clear of worms if gorse was used as their fodder. Some think it was the coarse material that scraped them clear, especially from the 'bots', which were the larvae of bot flies. The insect lays its eggs on the coat whence they were licked off to hatch in the stomach and attack the wall. The presence of alkaloids such as ulexine in the Furze may have a part to play in this vermifuge action. Little research has been conducted on the alkaloids and their toxicity, for gorse, and so we should treat the shrub with respect. There is the possibility that in large amounts they might accelerate the heart rate and so anybody with a heart condition would be best to avoid consumption, such as home-made gorse flower wine.

So, for heritage interest only, the following remedies occur in the Anglo-Saxon medicinal texts. Of course that makes them very old by our standards but medicine has always been very traditional and so some of the remedies are going to be far older than the Saxons; those people simply brought it forward into their own age. Just because they are recorded in writing does not mean that they *originated* in the later Saxon period. Some of the content in these manuscripts comes clearly from the early Saxon pagan period of the 5th and 6th centuries but in all probability was not new even then but give us a glimpse into the Iron Age culture. Similarly, references to 'pennyweight' should not be taken to imply that the remedy dates from the age of coinage. All that said, let us look at the text known as *The Old English Herbarium Manuscript V* wherein we find the gorse recipes in section 142.[38] In the Old English gorse is *gorst* and the text equates this with *tribulum*, reflecting Latin influence and maybe indicating that the original source was Mediterranean. The first recipe is for an external poultice: *"For great heat of the body take this plant 'tribulum' pounded, lay it thereto."* The second recipe is *"For foulness and rottenness of the mouth and gums take this plant 'tribulum' boilt, pounded with honey, it heals the mouth and the gums."* Thirdly, *"For that stones grow in the bladder take the seed of this same plant while green, pounded; give it to drink, it takes effect well."* Fourthly, *"for an adder's bite take five pennies' weight of this same plant's seed while green, pounded, give it to drink; also take the plant with it's seed, pounded; lay it to the wound, it releases him from danger."* Recipe number five says *"also, this same plant's seed drunk in wine is curative against a draught of poison."* Lastly, *for fleas take this same plant with its seed boilt, jump into the house, it kills the fleas."*

Intriguingly gorse was used as a treatment for adder bites (ineffectual) since both share the same habitat – an idea later to be Christianised in the belief that God provided cures alongside problems. Another example was saying that God grows docks next to stinging nettles because rubbing a dock leaf into the sting neutralises its effect.

Broom

While the gorse is thought to be relatively safe, the same cannot be said for the broom. When the heathland folk needed medicines they had a powerful ally in the broom, provided they treated it wisely. Our earliest indications of its medicinal usage date from Saxon times. Later in the Middle Ages the famous Welsh physicians of Myddfai used it for the suppression of urine: *"Take broom seed, counting nine and devoting the tenth to God; grind the seed into fine meal and take in drink, or as a confection in boiled honey. If a woman or a maid should do this neither pain nor abscess will ever take in her mammae."*[39]

Such uses were not peculiar to Wales. Broom gets entries in other medieval herbals, on the Continent, such as those of Passau 1485, *Hortus Sanitatis* 1491, *Grete Herbal* 1516. By 1618 it was in the British Pharmacopoeia although soon afterwards increased knowledge of other plants meant Broom was to some extent superseded. Nevertheless, broom is the only native member of the pea family to become an official British drug, with sixteen preparations still being listed in the 1993 British Pharmacopoeia.

It was cultivated first as a medicine long before fashions in gardening started to include such shrubs for their aesthetic value. Medicinal products have included Flores Genistae or Flores Scoparii from the flowers, Succus Scoparii from the fresh sap; Fluid Extract of Broom, Infusion of Broom, Decotions of Broom and Scoparii Cacumina from the tops and Sal Genistae, from the salts in the ashes of burnt tops which were treated as lye and drunk down with a glass of wine. There are home remedies containing broom still in use today but always consult a qualified herbalist before trying these for yourself. For one thing broom is toxic. Broom should definitely be avoided by anyone who is pregnant due to its oxytoxic activity, and, by anyone with high blood pressure as it is hypertensive and will affect the heart and respiration. It can also upset the stomach and bowels, for which it has been exploited as an emetic and a purge. It is variable though, like most herbs, and as William Withering pointed out back in the 18th century, it can be quite drastic with one patient while having little effect upon another.

Broom has long been taken as a diuretic, to stimulate the kidneys into removing excess fluid from the body and thereby flush out the

kidneys and bladder when they had
problems. The liver responds at the same
time. As diuresis works it affects the
lymphatic system making Broom useful for
dropsy – Johnson[40] reported that the Swedish
army was cured of dropsy by it, following a fever
epidemic in 1759. Gout too is cleared by the diuresis and for this
broom was used even by royal physicians, according to Gerard:
*"That worthie Prince of famous memorie Henrie 8 King of England
was woont to drinke the distilled water of Broom flowers against
surfets, and diseases thereof arising."* There was the alternative of
compounding the flowers into hog's lard to make an ointment for
external application to painful gouty parts.

Yellow jaundice was treated with it too, in common with many
other yellow flowers, since the colour was believed, according to the
Doctrine of Signatures, to be an indication from god that this was His
intended purpose for the plant. It must have been foul as enough
flowers had to be boiled in milk to make it very bitter. It was curdled
with vinegar and, if you were lucky, spiced to hide the taste. You
were supposed to get half a pint of this down you first thing every
morning for a week. It must have been just as bitter from those
physicians who prescribed it mixed with equal amounts of dandelion
root. Easier, no doubt, were the doses of ashes of broom, as per
K'Eogh's Irish herbal: *"The ashes infused in white wine powerfully*

48

provokes urine, and are good for jaundice."[41] People today still have childhood memories of broom medicine for yellow jaundice and testify to its unpleasantness.

For black jaundice (the name changes with the colour of the skin depending upon the disorder) broom was the prime remedy: "*T many handfuls (as you thinke good) of the dried leaves of Brooni gathered and brayed to powder in the moneth of May, then take unto each hand full of the dried leaves one spoonful and a halfe of the seed of Broom braied into powder: mingle these together, and let the sicke drinke thereof each day a quantity first and last, until he find he some ease. The medicine must be continued and so long used until it be quite extinguished: for it is a disease not very suddenly cured, but must by little and little be dealt withal,*" wrote Fitzherbert in his *Book of Husbandry*, in 1534.

Compounds in the broom alter the heart rate, the tension of the blood vessels and the blood pressure. Under professional care it is useful for tachycardia and functional palpitations and even heart failure, especially when associated with low blood pressure; and for when this causes oedema, or when patients are in shock. The way it causes small blood vessels to constrict has made it useful in cases of women's problems, from excessive menstruation to breast tumours. It was believed there were separate broom plants for men and women's problems, so from the South West, where broom is called bannel in Cornish, come references to he-bannels and she-bannels (how to distinguish them not discovered) just as there were he-heathers (*Calluna*) and she-heathers (*Ericas*).

The chief agent at work in these cases is the sparteine, discovered in 1851 by Stenhouse who also found that most occurred in plants growing in full sun and in early spring (May) before flowering. Such compounds can depress the heart and nervous system, to the state of paralysis but when sparteine comes under attack by acids in the body it becomes oxysparteine, useful as a heart stimulant. The ashes or sulphate salts of sparteine are now used as an antidote to some poisons including snake venom and wasp stings (and with a foreign reputation against rabies). Perhaps the heathland folk used it against their bee stings: it would have been the most effective treatment to hand. It is the best heathland vermifuge, for killing bodily vermin. A tablespoonful of a potion taken on an empty stomach shifts

49

roundworms (and probably everything else). Externally, apply oil in which crushed tops have been boiled for *"the surest medicine to kill lice of the head or body, if any,"* wrote Nicholas Culpeper in 1653.

If it kills worms and lice then we should realise this plant contains active compounds and should take care. It is these compounds that can make broom an effective medicine simply because they stimulate bodily changes but of course there is the danger that by consuming too much then symptoms of poisoning will arise. As broom affects the heart this is a serious consideration. The plant warns us that it contains toxins by its bitter taste, which is a common characteristic of a wide range of poisonous plants and is believed to be the reason why we developed taste buds for bitterness on our tongues.

Over the years a range of compounds have been isolated and given names such as cytisine, genistein, lupinidine, sarothamnine scoparine and sparteine, although some of these may be synonyms for each other or else act in the same ways. The important one is the quinolizidine alkaloid called sparteine (plus isosparteine), which affects the electro-conductivity of the heart muscle, affecting its rhythms. That can be dangerous and so can the ways the compound can interact with cardiac medicines that a person might be taking also. People with cardiac problems should avoid consuming this plant, including wine made from the flowers, since the toxins are found throughout the plant including the flowers. In the past the flowers have been added to beer to increase its intoxicating effects. Those who are pregnant should avoid broom since the sparteine stimulates uterine contractions and was used officially for this during the 1970s. It was soon discontinued due to the toxic side effects. The other important compound in broom is scoparin or scoparoside which increases urination and has been used officially as a diuretic. This treatment, in the 18th century attracted the attention of Dr William Withering, who was looking into treatments for dropsy. This led him to realise and promote the value of foxgloves. They yield four cardiac poisons used extensively in today's medicines. Further research is still needed before we can understand fully the toxicity of broom so be wary of it and be aware also that broom seeds can occur as substitutes for hops, coffee and capers and in some herbal medicines.

Broom is the only significant poisonous plant on the heathlands but having said that, it is not powerful in small doses and so should give no cause for alarm to visitors to the heathlands. Its tough stringy stems are not the sort of thing children are going to pick and munch as they walk along. Riders need not worry either since it takes over 11kg of broom to poison a horse, or so says popular tradition.

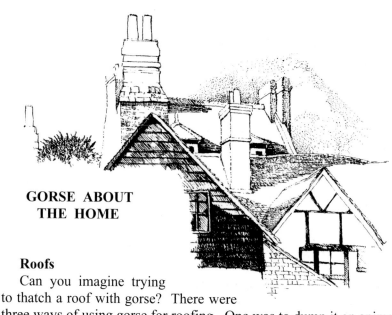

GORSE ABOUT
THE HOME

Roofs

Can you imagine trying to thatch a roof with gorse? There were three ways of using gorse for roofing. One was to dump it on animal shelters in the fields as a primitive covering, where it probably trapped some of the warm rising air but wouldn't have kept out heavy rain. Secondly mature gorse bushes were fired in the spring and left for the summer rains to clean the blackened trunks ready for an autumn harvest. These were then used as roof timbers for small spans. Modern floras say the shrub grows to two metres "or more" which must have been a lot more in former times as some roof timbers have been recorded at around five metres (in Ireland). The shorter, thinner timbers were used as the lesser horizontal roof members between the main beams to support more conventional thatch. This was sometimes developed into a woven mesh to which the thatch was sewn as per usual. Between this mesh and the thatch a layer of twiggy gorse could be placed to trap warm air and to stop dirt falling through if the roof was being covered with turfs, which would be placed soil side downwards. The spines were also a deterrent to sparrows and other intruders into the thatch.

Broom twigs have also been recorded as thatching material in the north of England and in Scotland, particularly the Highlands.[42]

Buildings

Builders sometimes employed chopped gorse as bonding material in cob walls, plaster, and the daub of 'wattle-and-daub' walling. Important though it was, little can be said about daub since records are so scarce. We can learn a lot about building materials from records of their purchase, as entered in the account books of the building concerned. Such records were only ever made for high status buildings or for the very wealthy who looked after their money by employing clerks to keep account of it. Consequently we read about quality daub made from materials that had to be bought in, such as hay, straw and animal hair, to the exclusion of any materials that could be provided freely by the estate, such as gorse. The records do teach us what an array of local dialect names was in use for the whole operation, from the names of the materials to the occupation of plasterer, and so it is possible that there are some more records in archives waiting to be recognised for what they are.[43] On the whole, we have little contemporary documentary evidence for what a farmer actually used for constructing his home and farm buildings. We have to rely on the archaeologist for that and with so much regard being paid to old buildings nowadays this information is being published annually in all the different site reports.

A mix similar to daub, and more likely to contain coarse gorse, was pounded into the potholes of the highway. Records for that are likely to be post-Elizabethan, and in particular in documentation relating to the very poor. The poorest heathland folk supplemented their meagre living by repairing roads for the turnpike trusts etc. Record books from the workhouses are a good place since the inmates were expected by the ratepayers to be employed gainfully.

Chimneys and Wells

When it came to sweeping chimneys, dragging a gorse bush down with a rope was a good way of shifting soot. If two pieces of bush, with the tops outwards, were tied in the centre of the rope then it could be shunted up and down the chimney between a worker on the roof and one in the hearth. In non heathland areas Holly was used instead. These practices persisted until the early 1960s in Surrey. Wells were cleaned similarly but the gorse bush had to be heavily weighted to send it plunging down with enough force to scrape the sides effectively; fine going down but hard work getting it up again.

Beds

Yes, gorse was used for making beds! The best description found dates from the 1890s with observations of the turf homes of the heathlanders (who were called 'heathers'; pronounced heethers). One end of the 'bungalow' had a board on end stretching right across the room and rising about nine inches. It was set forward of the wall by the desired width of the bed being made. Behind the board was backfilled densely with gorse tops. With the rigid spines going in all directions there was no possibility of flattening this layer and so it acted a bit like springs under the bed. More importantly, it enabled air to circulate and help keep the bed in sanitary condition. On top of the gorse was added a layer of heather bundles, meaning Ling, *Calluna vulgaris*. Each bundle was tied with a 'cord' made of heather stems and knotted with a special heather knot. This first layer was set at right angles to the end wall and then a second layer was added parallel to the end wall and then a third layer which

54

reverted to being at right angles again. Next it was padded with a layer of dead bracken. That would have been very uncomfortable to sleep on so it was topped off with a big palliasse, which they had made themselves out of hemp fabric, stuffed with 'hay' that would have been the dry foliage shed each autumn by the Purple Moor Grass, *Molinia caerulea*. The whole family slept on that together. It looks as though separating the genders didn't reach these homes until after 1800. Having the whole family in there would have been inclusive of the incontinent and so there was a need for good drainage. The coarse materials of the bed provided that, with only the palliasse needing to be spread outside over a bush each day. Should the sand floor beneath get wetted, the patch was scraped out and replaced. Theoretically, only the people with the right to take minerals off the land should have been able to re-sand but doubtless nobody heeded that for the amount required. It was the commercial seller who needed the right. He took, washed and sold sand as a scouring agent for floors, greasy pots and sweaty armpits. He was also the proverbial sand-man who sprinkled sand into the eyes of little children who did not fall asleep straight away at bed-time.

For a long time it seemed that only the heathlanders who had such sleeping accommodation but it now looks as though it is another example of an idea that slid down the social scale from top to bottom. Back in the Middle Ages a gorse mattress was a luxury for some of the wealthy at least. For example, in the building accounts of a house at Cardigan (wealthy enough to compile such accounts) in 1428, is the entry "*slyddys de gorst ad implenda lecta.*"[44]

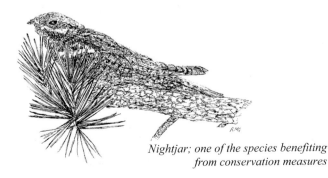

Nightjar; one of the species benefiting from conservation measures

GORSE ON THE FARM

Stacks

Hay and corn stacks were often built upon a foundation layer of gorse. It is said that this was to deter vermin but rats and mice are good jumpers and corn stacks were very motivating. A better reason was to improve drainage and air circulation underneath to prevent a soggy wasteful bottom layer. When stacks were not built circular then gorse was also built into the corners to protect them from abrasion by passing carts but more importantly, to deter livestock from using the corners as weak points at which to begin feeding.

Fertilizer and compost

Gorse and broom have nodules of bacteria on their roots to put nitrogen back into the soil and so they were grown as a natural way of fertilizing the land. When they were ripped out of the ground they left the root nodules behind to fertilize the subsequent crop. To this end they were grown as an undercrop of cereals and with hay, especially if the land was destined t lie fallow the following year, allowing a crop of gorse to be harvested. Overlapping the cycles in this way was obviously sound economic sense. Countless old field maps bear the name 'Furze Field' but these should be interpreted with caution. In the absence of other evidence it will not be clear whether this records temporary or permanent usage, or whether the name has been handed down for generations or whether it records the usage during the year of mapping. Back in the 17th century John Evelyn, through his *Silva,* was exhorting fellow landowners to use gorse not only to improve their land but as a lucrative crop. He reported *"a worthy correspondent of mine"* claimed the profit from gorse was greater than from an equal area of the best wheatland. Presumably Evelyn doubted this for he made it possible to identify his source, saying, *"If this be questioned .... the Scene is within a Mile of Hereford, and proved by anniversary Experience, in the*

Lands, as I take it, of a Gentleman who is now one of the Burgesses for that City." When furze land was returned to the plough the bigger roots or 'moots' were gathered to serve as another type of fuel. They burn bright and cleanly and so were popular in domestic hearths and cooking ranges and lasted far into the 20th century.

Harrowing

After ploughing, gorse served for the final harrowing of a fine tilth before seeding. The bushes were tied behind a draught animal and once weighted down with logs, were dragged across the field. Even when 'proper' harrows became commonplace gorse was tied underneath so thickly as to hold the tines clear of the ground for a finer tilth than with the tines alone. It saved work too since to get a good tilth with a tined harrow required working the fields twice, at right angles to each other. A hand-held branch is still good for scratching the surface for seeds requiring firm soil beneath them, such as lawn seed.

Bedding

Gorse tops were used also as animal bedding – yes bedding! It was put down as a base layer in the stalls and covered with a thick layer of material such as bracken, rushes or heather to insulate against the spines before a final covering of hay or straw. The dense spiny gorse in the bottom trapped air to increase the warmth in the stalls and improve drainage. When soiled heavily it was renewed, (the back end more frequently than the front) and then stacked, with or without layers of soil, ready to be spread on the fields. Alternatively it was thrown down n yards and lanes to be pulverised by stock and traffic. This gorse compost was favoured for potatoes, once they had arrived. It is rich in potash which promotes big tubers.

Protection

Gorse thickets were created to double up as protection for game, bee hives, lambing folds, etc. Once established they could be kept trim by allowing livestock to browse them.

Bee hives needed protection from the worst of the weather, especially if the heath caught the summer gales from off the sea. Recesses cut into a bank of gorse were just the place. Even the lee of a gorse hedge was better than nothing and such hedges were popular in counties like Cornwall because they would grow in defiance of salt winds. Apparently not all such hedges were left to the elements to stunt and prune for Evelyn reminded his Cornish readers not to waste clippings from their gorse hedges. He also drew attention to the value of this sort of protection as game cover, which was important right across the southern heathlands to East Anglia where the same usage was recorded by Chadwick. Similarly, gorse was cut and forced into gappy bottoms of poor hedges to control animals, whether livestock escaping or predators invading. It was buried with tree seeds, such as valuable Walnuts, to deter rodents from burrowing down and eating them and when the saplings were planted out dead gorse tops were piled around them as protection against browsing cattle and deer. Sprigs were also pushed into household gaps to keep rodents out.

Drains
Twiggy gorse tops were laid in land drains, to keep the soil open and free-draining into the earthenware drainpipes.

Odds and Ends
All in all, Furze has been an extremely valuable plant – so much so that the Church came to accept it as payment for tithes. Uses, extra to those detailed above, have included making lye and soap from ashes after firing, instead of, or with, the more usual bracken. Wine can be made from the flowers but this is perhaps best avoided due to possible toxicity, until the active compounds in gorse have been analysed fully. The flowers were used to dye hens' eggs as Easter eggs and the mature stems were made into walking sticks and hurleys for the Irish sport.

58

BROOM FOR FOOD AND DRINK

Warning – The following is recorded for historical interest and would be potentially harmful to some people if they tried it today.

Young tops, buds, flowers, pods and seeds of the broom have all been used in culinary ways and not just by the poor heathland people. As a delicacy they rose to the highest point of social life when broom tops were served at the coronation of James VII of Scotland/James II of England.

Usually it was the young buds that were harvested so that at the end of the Elizabethan age John Gerard recorded they were *"to be gathered and laid in pickle or salt, which afterwards being washed or boiled are used for salads as capers be and eaten with no less delight."* [45]

A century later and John Evelyn included them in his book of salads[46] saying *"Broom-Buds, hot and dry, retaining the virtue of Capers, esteemed to be very opening, and prevalent against the Spleen and Scurvy: and being Pickled, are sprinkled among Sallets, or eaten of themselves."* As for being good against scurvy, caused by too little vitamin C, this would have been one of the few antiscorbutic herbal treatments available on the heathlands. Scurvy was a common and nasty problem in the past and should not be thought of simply in terms of sailors or simply as a skin disease. The full impact is quite horrendous.

The seeds when roasted have been used widely in Britain (and in France etc.) as a substitute for coffee. In 1862 Johnson[47] described them as "no bad substitute". This usage lasted long in Scotland, where there were fewer alternative substitutes than in the south country. Down south it is to be wondered whether the heathland folk ever bothered with this when there were so many smugglers snaking their packhorses through the heather trails after dark, to supply what was otherwise too expensive – coffee, tea, brandy, lace, tobacco and so forth.

BROOM FOR BROOMS

Broom is distinct for having the same name as the artefact made from it. When the shrub was classified in the genus *Sarothamnus* the name comes from two Greek words meaning broom and shrub while the species name *scoparius* comes from the Latin *scopa* for a brush. This should therefore be an important section of this study but alas very few references have been found for it. These refer to 'green' broom which was crucial since the young green stems are pliant for sweeping whereas ageing or dead stems go hard and brittle. Material was made up into besoms the same as birch and heather and these persisted in use until the late 19th century. When Gertrude Jekyll published her *Old West Surrey* in 1904 she records a labourer reminiscing about a past employer:

"Quietest and best master I ever lived with. There was the red-brick kitchen floor. I used to flow he down with a green broom; the best of brooms for bricks; makes the floors red."

When tested for this study it proved to be true – after several brushings at intervals. It has been suggested that this is due to the broom storing vital calcium, as crystals, in the stems and that these are then brushed into the algae dulling the bricks whereupon the alkalinity of the calcium kills the algae, leaving the bricks smart clean red.

As said, *green* broom was crucial and gave rise to the proverb, *"The green new broom sweepeth clean,"* which was in writing by the 16th century. Green broom is this image that recurs through the medieval ballads wherein there are many references to going and cutting it:

There was an old man lived out in the wood,
And his trade was a-cutting of Broom, green Broom....

The recurrence of this imagery suggests that the practice was widespread and immediately understood by the audiences of the balladeers. Quite possibly these besoms therefore had a specific use and one that seems to have ended, or at least gone into sharp decline, at the end of the Middle Ages. It has not been possible to trace this so far but one suggestion is that the besoms were in demand from the woollen textile industry. When the cloth was stretched upon tenter hooks the shearers trimmed the nap to an even depth. The clippings would need to be swished off with something flexible that did not have the capacity to snag up further threads. A switch of broom would do that job admirably.

It is from the folklore that we learn that broom was indeed used fresh and cut during the flowering period.

Sweep the house with blossomed broom in May
And you'll sweep the head of the house away.

Or you will sweep your health or prosperity away, depending upon regional variations, but the taboo is widespread through the southern counties, from Devon to Sussex. There was a general taboo on bringing indoors flowering broom, whether as a besom, medicine, food or whatever. This is a belief held very strongly and still practiced today so it and so it raises questions as to whether broom-makers could sell their wares in May or during the flowering periods. Flowering Ling was banned similarly in Devon. At least birch was considered protective and not banned.

CHANGING LANDSCAPES

Once heathlands had been established as a major landscape feature of southern England by the farming practices of the prehistoric peoples they remained much the same for many centuries. The pattern of usage saw to that because the demand for turf fuel, grazing, broom-making materials etc. did not change significantly until very recent times. One exception to that general trend appears to centre on goats and in particular on their readiness to eat pine seedlings. Nothing else is so partial to having its food flavoured with turpentine. Thus the goat seems to hold the explanation as to why the Scots Pine becomes scarce in the fossil record after mid Saxon times. The Saxons (using the term in its broadest sense) held goats in high esteem – their great sky god, Thunor, had his chariot drawn by goats. He equates with Thor in the Norse beliefs. We know these gods were important to the heathlanders because heathside villages like Thursley in Surrey derive their names from them.

Goats provided valuable meat, milk, hide, hair, bone, sinew, fat and horn without being especially demanding. They can prosper by browsing the scrub of marginal land. By the mid period it looks as though they were clearing the pine seedlings to the point where Scots Pine disappear out of the heathland record. The pines return in the 17th century which is when goats fell from favour and numbers decreased. That is also the time when agricultural 'Improvements' started to change the overall landscape patterns that had remained almost static throughout the Middle Ages. After this period goats were kept only in small numbers rather than being herded across open heathlands and this was to the advantage of the pines. If this theory is correct then it indicates that the coming of the Normans made little difference to the relationship between pines and heathlands. The Normans were very keen on deer and the open heaths were seen as superb areas for the chase but they believed that goats and deer were incompatible. Apparently deer find the smell of goats repellent. Presumably by Norman times the goats had already broken the reproductive cycle of the pines and the other grazers simply kept the numbers down.

Pine cone seeds stripped by woodpecker

Pines affect the soil too. Compounds released from the decaying needles act as a growth retarder to erase competition for nutrients and moisture and so to walk unimpeded across a carpet of needles under the pines has been a visitor's delight since Victorian times. It does not delight the conservationist because it is at the expense of true heathland species. The problem is exacerbated today by the fecundity of modern pines. When the Government founded the Forestry Commission in 1919

the remit was to restock the country with fresh timber supplies to
replace those used up during the First World War. The Commission
set up experimental nurseries where they grew seed gathered far and
wide to see which genetic strains had the capacity to flourish upon
southern heathland soils, which were seen as potential sites for
forestation. This was successful but was not good news for the
heathlands. Not only were large areas planted over but the virile

64

If left alone, natural regeneration of bracken, birch and pine will shade and smother out the heathers and gorse. It can then produce a landscape much admired by visitors but it does not support the same diversity, or reflect our cultural heritage.

strains were soon seeding into adjoining heathlands. My childhood tree book says the Scots Pine will seed at 25 years old – now specimens on some heathlands are cone-bearing by six years old ! Seedlings need to be weeded out while still very young. That is easier said that done since the roots soon take a tenacious hold on the soil. There can also be public opposition to the removal of pine trees. Back in late Victorian times there are references from the Romantic Movement to *the cathedral pines* which seemed to sanctify them in people's minds (bearing in mind it was contemporary with the High Church Movement too). Additionally, prominent artists like Benjamin Leader, Myles Birket Foster and Helen Allingham were discovering the wild wilderness of the heathlands on their London doorsteps, aided by the expansion of the railways. Their rural portrayals, complete with pines, helped to fix these trees in the public mind. When Robert Louis Stevenson needed to proof read *Treasure Island* he retreated to Weybridge Common, up beside the railway station and we hear how there were expansive views beyond the massed flowering of the gorse. Today it is all treed over, with just a few scraggy gorse bushes gasping their last beside the road.

Much of that new tree cover, in common with most other sites, involves oak trees. These are a major problem. They now only suppress the gorse, broom and other heathland plants with their shade but they also destroy the very soil type that these other plants need. Leafmould from oaks changes the heathland 'podsol' to 'brown earth' and in that the heathland plants will not grow. Trying

to restore heathland where that has happened is no easy task and is best achieved by bulldozing off the surface soil back to the bare sand. Obviously that is drastic, scars the landscape, and inflames public opposition. Such is the national loyalty to 'good old English oak' that removing any oaks is highly contentious. Seedlings need to be removed very young before they

66

become emotive. Even that is no easy task since they too grip the soil with a back-breaking tenacity. One option is to reintroduce grazing livestock as per former times.

Grazing livestock need to be controlled by fencing and that is yet another contentious issue. Despite the provision of access points for the public there is still opposition, often virulent and highly organised, from local people who see it as a restriction to public access. There are also voices proclaiming 'commoners' rights' who forget that such a notion implies 'wrongs' as well and so it was, in the past when the landscape was worked, all activities were governed through the manorial courts. Where court records survive we find not only references to fencing but we find people brought before the court because they have *not* fenced their allocation of heathland:- *"W[illia]m Aylewyn, customary tenant, has not fenced his heathland, held from the Lord by the custom of the manor. He is ordered to fence the said heathland before next Easter, on pain of a fine of 6s 8d."*[48]

Entries such as these are primarily for livestock control, as can be seen so often in adjoining entries relating to crops being eaten by straying animals. They were fenced out. Gates were provided and these were known, in Surrey at least, as *hatches* and echo down to us in names like Whitwell Hatch, Tanners Hatch, etc.

Despite the administrative problems, the adoption of managed grazing has proved to be a sustainable way of conserving heathland. From it we are learning again what our ancestors once took for granted. Of particular value is the way that certain types of animal and even the differing breeds within the type, act as selective mowing machines. Cattle and ponies are heavy-footed and crush bracken crosiers as they rise in the spring. This is effective in controlling bracken and is used successfully on a number of sites managed by the National Trust, such as the Devil's Punch Bowl and Hindhead Common. Sheep on the other hand tend to tiptoe over bracken crosiers and are no help in controlling it. However, sheep can be very dainty feeders and very selective so have proved useful in maintaining the habitat for rarities such as the marsh gentian. All the browsers and grazers will take out tree seedlings and so maintain open heathland.

New Forest ponies are good at grazing off purple moor grass which is becoming so invasive on many sites at the expense of the desired heather. The trouble here stems from air pollution. Every year thousands of tonnes of nitrogen compounds are released into the air from plane and vehicle emissions, which dissolve into the rain drops, to fall as dilute nitrogen fertilizer. The purple moor grass loves it and flourishes. The heather hates it and becomes retarded, making its conservation all the more difficult. Furthermore, we are getting heather with a lot of top growth and poor root systems which leaves the cover far more susceptible to dying in prolonged drought. Attention is turning to the pollution as a possible cause. In particular, some researchers are concerned about the sharp decline in the number of toadstools each year (about 30% over the last 30 years according to some estimates) and they are wondering whether this is a consequence of the nitrogenous rain. It may be upsetting the balance of soil fungi. These fungi have symbiotic relationships with the vascular plants and help the latter to flourish. Maybe the poor

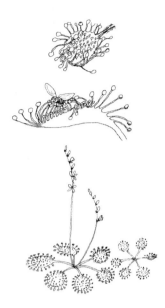

root systems are due to a decline in this relationship. It puts a question mark over the future of the insectivorous plants, such as the bladderworts, butterworts and the sundews illus.), which have evolved their carnivorous stratagems to overcome the shortage of nitrogen on heathlands. Will they now get choked to death on a glut of the stuff?

Conserving plants like the sundews is difficult because it likes disturbance; it likes wet areas that have been poached. Traditionally that was done by the livestock coming down to drink and there so there are descriptions from the 17th century of the blackish peaty soil turning crimson with the summer flush of the little sundews. There was so much of it that it was gathered commercially for use in brewing! Already noticeably in decline on some sites is the flowering of the bog cotton grass and the bog asphodel. It was thought this was due to excessive competition from other herbage in the absence of grazing but now we see flowering can be profuse where the area was trampled in the winter and the livestock must have provided this in the past.

All in all, the web of life on the heathlands is proving to be far more complicated and intricate than the visual simplicity of the landscape itself. It is very much a result of the landscape being *worked* for thousands of years. Protecting it from disturbance nowadays, in the name of conservation, is not going to suit all the species. In some places we must be more pro-active. These should still be *controlled* measures. Digging up swathes of turf might suit sand wasps, gorse and broom but that was not the way turf was taken in the past. We need to understand the past in order to temper the findings of modern science. Should we, for example, use fire in our conservation programmes? Certainly it has value on sites chosen carefully but it raises the question as to whether heathlands in the

69

past were burnt off regularly to promote new growth for grazing. There is no evidence for that. In the south the pressure on grazing, from millions of sheep, seems to have maintained the grazing without it becoming coarse and rank, needing burning off to stimulate regeneration. The scant references to heathland fires do not give us any inkling that this was part of a management strategy. Research into the effects of fire upon the soil shows that the soil recovers its balance of minerals quite quickly, with the exception of the essential phosphorus.

That takes up to twenty years to return to pre-fire levels and so we can be fairly certain that burning was not a frequent activity, if practised at all. That said, there is the designation of dead gorse stems as moots (discussed earlier) and the most likely cause of that would be fire. Today gorse thickets are a major fire risk but we need the thickets on sites frequented by the Dartford warbler (illus).

RMcG

70

One answer might be to grow the gorse in big 'islands' where the surrounding swathes can be less of a fire risk, such as young heather, but where firefighters can get right round their target. On some sites the gorse is kept young by regular coppicing, so reducing the build up on deep inflammable litter on the ground. That doesn't suit the Dartford warbler though, which likes to nest in the mature fuzzy-headed gorse and to forage in the deep litter below during the winter. It finds shelter from the cold there too. On sites where the Dartford warbler is not resident selected patches of mature gorse can be removed in sequence over several years. On some sites this is done with a controlled firing in the winter.

Of course the Dartford warbler is not the only concern. Gorse is part of a far broader web of life that includes, for example, the yellowhammer and the linnet. Where heathland adjoins farmland, birds like the yellowhammer tend to feed in the fields and nest on the heathland. The yellowhammer prefers sites with adjoining arable land since it has adapted to feeding on corn, whether the autumn/spring sowing or the summer maturing crop.

Yellowhammer

71

They fly into the heathland for breeding, liking to nest in the rank grasses and litter that can build up around the edge of the gorse clump or else they nest above ground in the lower branching, where the nest is protected and unseen under its spiny umbrella. Using the same locations to nest is the linnet which likes larger masses of gorse since this bird nests communally. Again they like to get into coarse grass and twiggery near ground level. They will even nest in marram grass where that, with gorse and broom, are being used for sand dune stabilisation. Linnets too will fly off to feed on adjoining farmland or in nearby gardens, taking a variety of seeds, supplemented with beetles, moths and caterpillars. Thus successful conservation of species associated with heathlands can depend upon the changing landscapes adjacent and in the case of agricultural land that is very much a changing landscape. It affects a wide range of species from lapwings and partridges to rooks.

Adaptation to environmental changes is a slow process and we hear continually that 'habitat loss' is thought to be the prime factor in the decline of so many species. The fact that so many species have adapted to the heathland habitat is evidence of man being active out there, working the land in a consistent manner. Such traditional practices have declined sharply and mostly disappeared during the 20th century, hence the large number of species that have become rarities during that time. Conservation therefore needs to be aggressive on many sites. Simply setting them aside as a 'safe haven' will not perpetuate the traditional web of life. Invading scrub takes over. That can be dealt with but other factors changing today's landscape, such as the nitrogen compounds from air pollution, are a far greater challenge. There are now heathland conservation projects all round the heathland counties, striving to save as much as possible. With so much emphasis upon wildlife it should not be forgotten that the habitat was made extensive and maintained by man. They are part of our cultural history; they are the coloured illustrations to the black and white text of the history books. Here we can still see the deserted prehistoric fields within their low banked boundaries and pause by the burial mounds of the people who depended upon them. The story

72

has never ended. It runs right through to the present, when thousands of acres are now used by the Ministry of Defence as military training grounds.

These are places where the past can be brought vividly to life to capture the imagination of visitors who in turn may well be more inclined to support the conservation measures, before it is too late.

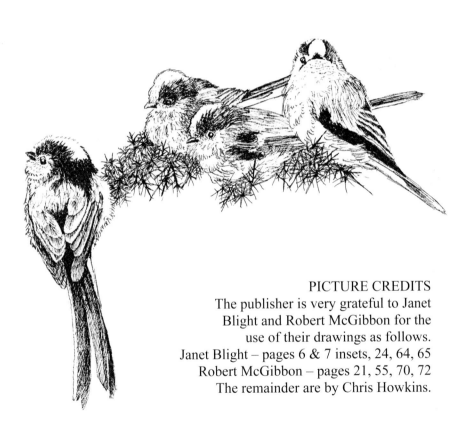

PICTURE CREDITS
The publisher is very grateful to Janet Blight and Robert McGibbon for the use of their drawings as follows.
Janet Blight – pages 6 & 7 insets, 24, 64, 65
Robert McGibbon – pages 21, 55, 70, 72
The remainder are by Chris Howkins.

THE YEAR'S HARVEST

A harvest could be taken off the heathlands and processed throughout the year, as illustrated in the table below. This table is, however, highly generalised. Not all the plants would be found on every heath and neither would all have been needed by any one community, even if they knew the full range of possibilities. Obviously seasonal and regional variations need to be taken into account, with regard to the months.

Plant \ Month	J	F	M	A	M	J	J	A	S	O	N	D
Birch (Sap)	▓	▓										
Birch (Brooms)	▓	▓	▓	▓	▓	▓	▓	▓	▓	▓	▓	▓
Ling (Brooms)	▓	▓	▓	▓	▓				▓	▓	▓	▓
Ling (Honey)							▓	▓				
Dodder							▓	▓				
Broom (Brooms)	▓	▓	▓	▓	▓	▓	▓	▓	▓	▓	▓	▓
Broom (Flowers)					▓	▓						
Broom (Thatch)					▓	▓		▓	▓			
Sundews						▓						
Erica (Honey)							▓	▓				
Bog Cotton					▓	▓						
Shallon (Fruits)									▓	▓		
Bog Bean				▓	▓	▓	▓	▓				
Sweet Gale					▓	▓	▓					
Bog Asphodel							▓	▓				
Bracken				▓	▓	▓	▓	▓	▓	▓		
Sphagnum	▓	▓	▓	▓	▓	▓	▓	▓	▓	▓	▓	▓
Gorse	▓	▓	▓	▓	▓	▓	▓	▓	▓	▓	▓	▓
Whortleberries							▓	▓				
Grazing	▓	▓	▓	▓	▓	▓	▓	▓	▓	▓	▓	▓

NOTES

[1] Additionally there is a related spiny shrub called Petty Whin (*Genista anglica* L.) which is excluded from this volume simply because I have never found any specific documentation in the context of the overview of this present study.

[2] John Evelyn, (1664), *Silva*, p8

[3] See Ronald Hutton (1996), *The Stations of the Sun: the Ritual Year in Britain;* OUP.

[4] Ann Marie Lafonte (1984); *Devon's Heritage: A Herbal Folklore,* Badger Books, Bideford. pp 40-1

[5] See Francis James Child (1882-9), *The English and Scottish Popular Ballads;* repr. Dover Pub. Inc. New York; 1965

[6] Child, F.J.ed; *The English and Scottish Popular Ballads,* 1882-89; 5 vols. Repr. Dover, New York, 1965. This ballad was recorded by the 16th century.

[7] As above.

[8] Roy Vickery, *A Dictionary of Plant Lore;* OUP; 1995, p.157.

[9] As above. p.156

[10] Geoffrey Grigson, The *Englishman's Flora;* Dent; 1987 ed. p.126

[11] This is not from the four Gospels chosen for inclusion in the New Testament. If it did occur in any of the other Gospels or scriptures then it refers to a totally different plant, the White Broom or Juniper, *Retama raetam,* which is a common shrub in desert wastes of Israel and Syria.

[12] For very readable and authoritative overviews of the prehistoric period, including refs. to contrary opinion, see;-
Pryor, Francis (1998); *Farmers in Prehistoric Britain;* Tempus; Stroud.
Pryor, Francis (2003); *Britain BC: Life in Britain and Ireland before the Romans;* HarperCollinsPublishers.

[13] For the place of heather in the history and economy of the heathlands see: Howkins, Chris (2004); *Heathers and Heathlands;* Chris Howkins Publication; Addlestone.

[14] Explained in detail in Howkins, *Heathers and Heathlands.*

[15] See Boston, Cecilia Lady; *The History of Compton in Surrey;* 1933; Wightman & Co. Ltd (1987 repr. by Compton Parochial Church Council used, pp 95-6)

[16] For William Lucas see John Harvey (1972); *Early Gardening Catalogues;* Phillimore; Chichester

[17] The Irish Farmers' Gazette, Vol 26; 1867 Dublin

[18] See website for Flora Celtica

[19] Evelyn, John (1664) *Silva*

[20] Stewart, Sheila; *Lifting The Latch;* p116

[21] See the Victoria County History, vol. I; p.367

[22] See *Surrey Archaeological. Collections.* Vol.61; 1964; pp.51-73

[23] See Chris Howkins (2006); *Poisonous Plants in Britain: a Celebration;* esp. ch.1 and ch.4

[24] Aubrey, John (1965) *The Natural History of Wiltshire*

[25] Varies according to the season but on average something in the order of 20,572 kJ/kg HHV (high heating value) and 6169 kJ/kg LHV (low heating value. For

detailed analysis (Spain) see Nunez-Regueira, Lisardo; Rodrigues Anon, J. A.; Proupin Castinersa, J. 1996. Calorific values and flammability of forest species in Galicia. Coastal and hillside zones. Bioresources and Technology. Oxford, U.K.: Elsevier Science Limited. 57(3): 283-289.

[26] Munster Farmers' Mag: Cork: Vol 1; 1812 p36

[27] From the translation housed in Liphook Public Library, Hants. Page 51; para 6. It does not specify for what these gloves were intended.

[28] Lucas, A.T.; (1960) *Furze:a Survey and History of its Uses in Ireland*; Dublin; p.49

[29] In round figures, the high heating value (HHV) is over 20,000 kJ/kg and the low heating value (LHV) is over 5,700 kJ/kg

[30] I am grateful to the Beeding Local History Society for drawing this to my attention.

[31] Johnson, C. P., (1862); *The useful Plants of Great Britain;* Robert Hardwick

[32] Chertsey Museum local archives, 'Chertseyana' Vol 1,79

[33] Stratton, H. J. M. (1990); *Ottershaw Through the Ages*; pub H.J.M.Stratton

[34] Gover, J. E. B. et al; (1934); *The Place-names of Surrey;*English Place-name Society 11; CUP.

[35] Jekyll, Gertrude (1904); *Old West Surrey*; Longmans, Green & Co.; p208

[36] I am grateful to Arthur Lunn for sharing his local history research for Pyestock.

[37] Freeman, G. (2005 ed.); *A History of Sunbury on Thames*; Sunbury and Shepperton Local History Society

[38] Numbering and translations as per Stephen Pollington (2000); *Leechcraft: Early English Charms, Plantlore and Healing*; Anglo-Saxon Books.

[39] Hoffmann, D. (1992), *Welsh Herbal Medicine*; Abercastle Publications; p.35

[40] Johnson, C. P. (1862); *The Useful Plants of Great Britain*; Robert Hardwicke. P.71

[41] K'Eogh, John (1735); *The Botanalogia Universalis Hibernica;* ed by Michael Scott; Aquarian Press; 1986; p.35.

[42] Barbara Fairweather (1984); *Highland Heritage*; Glencoe Folk Museum

[43] A good selection can be found in L. F. Salzman (1952); *Building in England down to 1540*; OUP; Ch XII, pp. 187-194.

[44] From L. F. Salzman (1952), *Building in England Down to 1540*; OUP; p.261.

[45] John Gerard (1597); *The Herball or General Historie of Plantes*

[46] John Evelyn (1699); *Acetaria;* entry no. 12

[47] Johnson, C. P. (1862), *The useful Plants of Great Britain,* Hardwicke

[48] From court records of Ludshott, Hampshire. 4th August 1462. Transcript held at Liphook library.

SELECT BIBLIOGRAPHY

AUBREY, John, *Natural History and Antiquities of the County of Surrey;* 1718-19, Repr. 1975, Kohler & Coombes, Dorking.

BECKETT, Kenneth and Gillian; *Planting Native Trees and Shrubs;* Garrold, 1979

BULLOCK, J.M., and N.R. Webb. 1995. Responses to severe fires in heathland mosaics in southern England. Biological Conservation 73, 207-214.

CHADWICK, L. *In Search of Heathlands;* Dennis Dobson; 1992

CHAPMAN, S.B., R.J.Rose, and M.Basanta. 1989. Phosphorus absorption by soils from heathlands in southern England in relation to successional change. J. Applied Ecology 26, 673-680.

CHILD, F.J.ed.; *The English and Scottish Popular Ballads.* 1882-89; 5 vols. Repr. Dover, New York, 1965

COOPER, M. R. and A. W. JOHNSON; *Poisonous Plants in Britain and their effects on Animals and Man;* HMSO; 1984

DIMBLEBY,G., *The Development of British Heathlands and their Soils;* Oxford; 1962

GERARD, John; *The Herball or Generall Historie of Plantes;* Thomas Johnson ed. 1636.

GIMINGHAM, C.H. Heathland Ecology. Chapman & Hall, London; 1972

GIMINGHAM, C.H., S.B.Chapman, and N.R.Webb. European heathlands. In *Ecosystems of the World*, Volume 9A: Heathland and Related Shrublands (R.L.Specht, ed.). Elsevier, Amsterdam; 1979

GODWIN, Harry, *History of the British Flora,* Cambridge University Press, 2nd ed. 1975

HARVEY, John., *Early Gardening Catalogues*; Phillimore 1972

HILL, Thomas, *The Gardenner's Labyrinth*; OUP Ed. 1975; 1577

HOFFMAN, D; W*elsh Herbal Medicine*; Abercastle Publications;1978

JEKYLL, Gertrude; *Old West Surrey*; Longmans; 1904.

K'EOGH, John, *Botanalogia Universalis Hibernica;* Cork; 1735.

LAFONT, A. *A Herbal Folklore;* Badger Books; Bideford; 1984.

LEWIS, William; *An Experimental History of the Materia Medica,* 4th ed. ed John Aitken, London 1791.

LUCAS, A. T., *Furze; A Survey and History of its Uses in Ireland;* Dublin 1960

MABEY, R.; *Flora Britannica;* Sinclair-Stevenson; 1996.

MARTINDALE : *The Extra Pharmacopoeia;* Pharmaceutical Press; 30th ed. 1993

PARKINSON, J., *Theatrum Botanicum.* 1640.

PARRY, J., *Living Landscapes – Heathland.* National Trust, 2003

POLLINGTON, Stephen; *Leechcraft: Early English Charms, Plantlore and Healing;* Anglo Saxon Books; 2000

RACKHAM, Oliver, *History of the Countryside,* Dent; 1986

STACE, C. *New flora of the British Isles;* Cambridge U.P. 1991.

VERA, F. W. M. ed; *Grazing Ecology and Forest History;* CABI Publishing; 2000

WEBB, N.R. 1986. Heathlands. Collins, London.

WEBB, N.R. 1990. Changes on the heathlands of Dorset, England, between 1978 and 1987. Biological Conservation 51, 273-286.

WEBB, N.R. 1994. Post-fire succession of cryptostigmatic mites (Acari, Cryptostigmata) in a Calluna-heathland soil. Pedobiologia 38, 138-145.

YOUNG, Geoffrey; *Traditional British Crafts;* Marshall Cavendish; 1989.

INDEX

80